D1330027

APPETIZING SLENDERIZING RECIPES

by **PATRICK J. CONWAY**
and **MARY ELLENWOOD PITTENGER**

Published by

CONWAY DIET INSTITUTE, INC.
COLUMBUS, OHIO

With many thanks to the other Pat.

Patrick J. Conway

And to my Mother who is enjoying a new
way of cooking.

Mary Ellenwood Pittenger

CONTENTS

Foreword   4

A Few Tips for the Cook   6

Conway 1000 Calorie Diet   8

Nutritional Values   12

Breakfasts   13

Lunches   19

Dinners   29

Vegetables   50

Desserts   62

Snacks & Soups   73

Beverages   81

Dressings & Spreads   87

Weekly Progress Chart   95

FOREWORD

This book contains hundreds of delicious recipes that should be an invaluable aid to the conscientious dieter. We believe it will help make dieting a pleasant and enriching experience with lasting results. Too many overweight people associate dieting with privation. We hope our recipes will help them realize that they can eat plentiful and delectable meals and still lose weight.

Calories are one of the most misunderstood aspects of nutrition. Calories are units of energy. When eaten but not consumed by activity, calories are stored in the body as fat. It is possible to eat relatively little food and become overweight. This can happen if the foods we eat are disproportionately high in calories. It is also possible to eat substantial quantities of food that are high in protein, minerals and vitamins but are very low in calories. When we do, then our bodies convert the stored body fat into energy and we lose weight.

The Conway 1000 Calorie Diet is a nutritionally balanced diet which will insure a substantial weight loss each week. Our recipes have been carefully designed to work with the Diet and to furnish three nutritious weight reducing meals a day. The vegetables in our recipes have been selected for their high vitamin, mineral and low calorie content. For this reason, especially generous portions are permitted at mealtimes or as snacks. Anyone who uses our recipes for breakfast, lunch and dinner and includes one glass of skimmed milk and three medium-sized fresh fruits daily in her diet, will have no difficulty in losing weight. Our experience is that anyone who follows our Diet and recipes exactly and does not substitute or change the method of preparation (such as frying instead of broiling) consistently loses about 2 pounds a week. But even more important, the dieter develops a new knowledge of foods and new tastes which will enable her to eat satisfying and delicious meals while retaining her new slimness for the rest of her life.

Dieters frequently ask about the importance of exercise as an aid to losing weight. Any form of physical activity consumes calories or stored body fat. So the more activity an overweight person engages in, the faster she will lose weight. A most desirable form of activity is walking. The advantages of walking are many; it is not too strenuous, it requires no special preparation, equipment or skill, it is inconspicuous and it's effective. A brisk walk of one-hour duration every day (you can break it into four 15-minute periods if you like) will burn up approximately one extra pound of body fat per week. We recommend increased physical activity in conjunction with dieting.

Since many of our recipes include the use of saccharin, we would like to draw your attention to recent Federal Drug Administration statements advising that prolonged and heavy usage of saccharin may be injurious to health.

Good health begins with a checkup. It is an excellent idea to check with your physician before losing weight. This is particularly important if you are taking medication of any kind or have a medical condition such as ulcers, heart disease, food allergies, diabetes or if you are pregnant. Your doctor should be aware of the change in your eating habits. He may wish to modify your diet or to change your medication as you lose weight.

A FEW TIPS FOR THE COOK

Losing weight requires change. A very good place to start is with food preparation. Our way of cooking may be different from what you have been doing. To change a weight-loss diet into a stand-still diet, we need only add 4 tablespoons of fat a day. It doesn't matter whether it's bacon fat, chicken fat, cooking oil or salad oil. So don't cheat yourself of a good weight loss by thinking that a little bit won't hurt. It can make a lot of difference.

Sweetener...start with about half the amount stated in a recipe, and then taste. If it's not sweet enough add more. When you can't decide if you need more, stop. It's the next drop that gives some people the bitter after taste.

You may use fresh onions or fresh green peppers instead of the dried ones in most recipes. The dried peppers are available all year around, with not much variance in price.

You can make your own herb vinegar by combining 1 cup of white vinegar with 1/2 teaspoon of your favorite herb. Heat to boiling, cool, cover and refrigerate for several days. Try different herbs for different flavor-tarragon, oregano, mint, dill, etc.

You can increase the iron content of meats from 100% to 400% by cooking them in a cast iron skillet and adding a small amount of acid - such as tomato juice, lemon juice or vinegar.

About one-third of the vitamins and minerals in canned products may be in the liquids. So store the liquids in the refrigerator and use instead of water in recipes calling for bouillon cubes.

Save the broth from boiled chicken. Always skim off the fat before using the broth. This makes a great base for many kinds of soup.

Always put water in the bottom of broiler pan when broiling steak. This makes for easier cleaning but even more important you can use a tablespoon of this broth to flavor vegetables. Be sure to skim off the fat before using. This broth is especially good if a bouillon cube is too salty for your taste.

6

Any recipe is one person's idea of the way she likes a particular dish. So, feel free to experiment. If you don't like horseradish, leave it out. If you want mace instead of nutmeg, put it in.

Your whole family is entitled to good nutrition. Our way of cooking and eating is good nutrition. If members of your family need extra calories to keep up their weight, serve side dishes such as potatoes, creamed peas, bread and butter. Just remember, these fattening foods are for them - not you. Your goal is to become "slim & trim" as quickly as possible.

THE CONWAY 1,000 CALORIE DIET

FOODS WE EAT TO LOSE WEIGHT

MEATS:

Broil, bake or roast meats, fish or poultry. Do
not fry or pan broil. Remove all visible fat before
eating. Do not eat gravies or sauces or use meat
tenderizers.

3 dinners per Week	4 Dinners per Week	Dinner Portion
beef (any cut)	chicken (without skin)	5 oz. cooked
lamb (any cut)	seafood (any variety)	7 oz. raw
	turkey (without skin) veal	9 oz. raw w/skin & bone

VEGETABLES:
May be eaten raw or cooked without fat or salad dressing, either at meals or between meals. Eat until
satisfied. Vary your selection frequently.

asparagus	fennel	radishes
bean sprouts	green and red	rhubarb
beet greens	pepper	sauerkraut
broccoli	kale	scallions
cabbage	lettuce	spinach
carrots	mushrooms	string beans
cauliflower	mustard greens	summer squash
celery	onions	turnips
chinese cabbage	parsley	watercress
cucumber	pimientos	wax beans
eggplant	pickles (dill or sour)	zucchini

FRUITS: Eat three(3) medium sized fruits a day.

apples	grapefruit	pineapple
apricots	melons	plums
berries (any kind)	oranges	pumpkin
cantaloupe	peaches	tangerines
	pears	tomatoes

PORTION:
1/2 medium sized cantaloupe = 1 fruit
1/2 small fresh pineapple = 1 fruit
2 inch wedge of honeydew = 1 fruit
4 oz. of juice = 1 fruit
1/2 cup berries = 1 fruit
1/2 medium sized grapefruit = 1 fruit

DAIRY:

Milk--Drink 1 glass (8 oz.) of skimmed milk or butter-
    milk daily.
Eggs--Cook in shell, poach or scramble without fat.
Cheese--Hard or soft in quantities specified in Eating
    Pattern.

BREAD:
Two (2) slices of white enriched, whole wheat, cracked
    wheat or rye bread daily at meals specified in Eating
    Pattern.

SEASONING:
Use as desired.

bouillon
herbs--such as garlic, oregano
    thyme, dill, paprika
horseradish (red or white)
lemon, lime
mustard
pepper

salt (use sparingly)
saccharin
soy sauce
spices--such as cinna-
    mon, ginger, cloves,
    mint nutmeg
tomato juice (in cooking)
vinegar

FOODS WE DO NOT EAT OR DRINK
WHILE LOSING WEIGHT

MEATS:
bacon
beef tongue
corned beef
fat
frankfurters (all kinds)

pork
processed luncheon meats
sardines
skin of turkey or chicken
smoked fish or meat

VEGETABLES:
beans and lentils
beets
brussels sprouts
corn
lima beans
olives
okra
parsnips

peas
nuts
potatoes
rice
winter squash (hubbard,
    acorn, butternut)
yams

FRUITS:

avocado
bananas
cherries
dried fruits (including prune juice)

grapes
papayas
watermelon

DAIRY:

butter
cream (sweet or sour)
cream cheese

margarine
yogurt
whole milk

BREADS/GRAINS:

biscuits
cake
cereals
chips
cookies
crackers
doughnuts
macaroni

matzos
muffins
pancakes
pretzels
rolls
spaghetti
waffles

BEVERAGES:

beer
wine
gin
vodka
cordials

whiskey
ginger ale
cola drinks
sugar drinks

SWEETS:

candy
chocolate
coconut
honey
ice cream
ices
jam
jelly

jello
peanut butter
pies
pudding
sugar
syrups

SEASONINGS/CONDIMENTS:

gravy
ketchup

mayonnaise
oil
salad dressing

EATING PATTERN
NEVER SKIP A MEAL.

BREAKFAST

4 oz. of fruit juice or 1/2 grapefruit
1 egg   OR   1 oz. hard cheese   OR   2 oz. soft cheese

	1 oz. hard cheese	2 oz. soft cheese
	Swiss	Cottage
	Cheddar	Pot
	American	Farmer
	Muenster	Ricotta

1 slice of white enriched, whole wheat, cracked
   wheat or rye bread
Beverage (coffee, tea)

LUNCH:
3 oz. (cooked) of seafood, cottage cheese or chicken
Vegetables (green salad and/or cooked vegetables)
1 slice of white enriched, whole wheat, cracked
   wheat or rye bread
Beverage (coffee, tea)

DINNER:

3 Times per Week	4 Times per Week
5 oz. (cooked)	5 oz. (cooked)
Beef	Chicken
Lamb	Seafood
	Turkey
	Veal

Vegetables (green salad and/or cooked vegetables)
Beverage (coffee, tea)

DAILY:

At meals **or** between meals:
   1 glass (8 oz.) skimmed milk or buttermilk
   3 fruits

ANYTIME SNACKS (OPTIONAL)

   Vegetables
   Bouillon (with vegetables if desired)
   Sugar--free carbonated drinks
   Sugarless Gum
   Gelatin (artificially sweetened)
   Coffee, Tea
   Water

NUTRITIONAL VALUES OF CONWAY 1000 CALORIE DIET

	Recommended Daily Allowances *	CONWAY DIET (Daily Average)
VITAMIN A	5000 I.U.	21,580 I.U.
NIACIN	13.0 milligrams	24.0 milligrams
RIBOFLAVIN	1.5 milligrams	2.0 milligrams
THIAMIN	1.0 milligrams	1.15 milligrams
VITAMIN C	55.0 milligrams	268.0 milligrams
IRON	18.0 milligrams	19.2 milligrams
CALCIUM	0.8 grams	0.9 grams
PROTEIN	55.0 grams	92.0 grams
CARBOHYDRATE	none	108.0 grams
FAT	none	24.0 grams

* American Medical Association Recommendations for Adult Women.

FOOD SOURCE OF CALORIES		CALORIC VALUE OF MEALS (Daily Average)	
Carbohydrate	43%	Breakfast	18%
Protein	36%	Lunch	24%
Fat	21%	Dinner	39%
		Snacks/Fruits/Milk	19%

BREAKFAST

BREAKFAST CHEESE DANISH

1 slice toast	1/8 t. vanilla
2 oz. cottage cheese	pinch of nutmeg
1/8t. cinnamon	artificial sweetener
	(to taste)

Combine cheese and spices in blender or beat well with mixer.
Spread on toast and place in broiler until warmed. You'll
love this with apple slices, crushed pineapple, cinnamon
and nutmeg on top of the cheese. This is a delicious breakfast! Remember to deduct fruit from your daily fruit allowance.

HEARTY OMELET

1 small can sliced mushrooms	dehydrated onion flakes
1 egg	to taste
1/2 green pepper diced fine	oregano
1/4 C. tomato juice	salt, pepper

Beat all ingredients in a deep bowl with a fork. Pour into
heated non-stick fry pan. Brown on one side, turn carefully and brown the other side.

FRENCH TOAST

1 slice of bread	artificial sweetener
1 egg	

Soak the slice of bread in the well-beaten egg. Add artificial sweetener to taste. Broil on both sides. Sprinkle
with cinnamon. Also try apple slices or crushed fruit from
your daily allowance.

STRAWBERRY SHORTCAKE

1 slice of bread, diced	Dash of sweetener
½ C. fresh strawberries,	Fluff (see Desserts)
mashed	

Mix strawberries and sweetener, pour over bread. Cover with
desired amount of Fluff. This is a breakfast or lunch
recipe, so deduct the Fluff from your daily milk allowance.
Don't forget to include your egg for breakfast. This recipe
includes 1 fruit allowance.

If you are having this at lunch, don't forget your fish
allowance.

LUMBERJACK SCRAMBLED BREAKFAST

2 oz. Zippy Zero (see   1 or 2 oz. sliced mushrooms
   Dressings & Spreads)   1 egg, beaten
1 green onion, minced   oregano, salt, pepper

Mix together, pour into heated teflon or cast iron skillet.
Stir until your scrambled egg is cooked, about 5 minutes.

Have a piece of toast with this, and you're well equipped
for the morning's work!

CHEESE-APPLE RING

1 piece toast   1 small apple, cored, cut
1 oz. hard cheese   into 6 rings

Place cheese on toast, top with apple rings dusted with
nutmeg and cinnamon. Broil until cheese bubbles up. This
is a breakfast that has "staying" power. Deduct apple from
your daily fruit allowance.

PIZZA

1 piece toast   1/2 small can mushrooms,
1 oz. hard cheese   drained
1 T. Zippy Zero (see   Oregano
   Dressings & Spreads)   Garlic powder (optional)

Put your toast covered with cheese on an aluminum foil pie
pan. Top with mushrooms, drizzle the Zippy Zero over all,
sprinkle with oregano and garlic powder as desired. Who
said Slim and Trim followers can't have pizza?

PICKLED EGGS

4 eggs   Artificial sweetener to taste
1/2 C. vinegar   Red food coloring
1/2 C. water

Place eggs in a small pan, cover with cold water, and heat
until the water boils. Turn off the fire. Put a lid on
the pan and let it set right there for 25 minutes. Cool
the eggs under the cold water, crack shells all around,
and peel. Heat vinegar, water, food coloring, and sweetener
to a boil. Put eggs in a small jar, and pour the hot
solution over them. Let set in refrigerator to chill, and
enjoy your breakfast egg with toast any morning. Of course
this is enough eggs for 4 people 1 breakfast, or 1 person
for 4 breakfasts. And this breakfast is always ready to
eat! If you've made Sweet Dill Slices lately, (see vegetables) you can simple use 1 cup of that solution and color
it. Very good eating!

14

STRAWBERRY PIE FOR BREAKFAST

CRUST:
4 slices bread, toasted and   1 t. vanilla
  crumbed in blender   1 t. liquid sweetener
1/4 C. water

FILLING:
1 package unflavored   1 T. lemon juice
  gelatin   1/4 t. salt
1/4 C. cold water   8 oz. cottage cheese
3/4 C. boiling water   4 drops of yellow food
Sweetener to equal 1/2   coloring
  C. sugar   2 C. strawberries, sliced

To make crust, combine liquids and fold in bread crumbs
with a fork, until the crumbs are moistened. Lightly
press onto bottom and sides of a 9" pie plate. Bake at
400 about 10 minutes, or until crust is lightly browned.
Cool.

To make filling, soften gelatin on cold water, dissolve in
boiling water. Add sweetener, lemon juice, salt, and
cottage cheese. Whip in blender until no lumps remain--
about 30 seconds. Add food coloring and chill until thick.
Then whip in blender about 10 seconds, and fold in the
strawberries. Spoon into crust, and chill in refrigerator
2 hours, or overnight. One fourth of the pie equals 1
fruit, 1 bread and 1 serving of cottage cheese for breakfast.
What a way to lose weight!

LATE SUNDAY BREAKFAST

1/2 can asparagus, drained   1 pickled egg
          1/2 recipe Dressing Vinaigrette

Marinate asparagus overnight in dressing in the refrigerator. At breakfast time, drain asparagus, put it on a leaf
of lettuce, and slice the pickled egg over it. Lovely to
look at, refreshing to eat.

BREAKFAST AU GRATIN

1 serving cauliflower, broc-   1 oz. hard cheese
  coli, asparagus, etc.   1 slice bread

Put drained, cooked vegetable on an aluminum foil pie pan.
Heat through. Put bread and cheese through blender together. Sprinkle cheese-crumb mixture on top of hot vegetables.
and bake or broil until the crumbs are toasted.

EGG NOG AND MELBA TOASTIES

1 egg
1/3 C. dry powdered milk
1/2 C. water

Sweetener to equal 1 T. sugar
1/2 t. vanilla or any flavor
  extract

3 ice cubes

Mix all together in blender. Serve icy cold. You might
like to add 1/2 C. orange juice to this too. Recipe equals
1 glass of milk.

MELBA TOASTIES: Slice bread to half its thickness. Bake
300 about 20 minutes, or until golden.

Be sure the bread is at least one day old. Using a sharp,
thin knife, start halving at each of the four corners,
advancing towards the center of the slice. Think UP as
you slice, and you'll get two thin slices every time!

SLIM & TRIM PANCAKES

If you really want a pancake, here are two different
versions, depending on whether you want to use an egg or
cottage cheese:

EGG CAKES:
1 egg
2 T. skim milk
1 slice bread, in pieces

CHEESE CAKES:
2 oz. cottage cheese
2 T. water
1 slice bread, in pieces

Put ingredients for chosen pancake in blender. For the
egg cakes you may like to add a drop of sweetener and a
dash of cinnamon. For the cheese cakes, try adding 1 drop
of yellow food coloring, and a drop of sweetener.

Make four small pancakes on a heated Teflon skillet. Brown
and turn carefully. Serve with Tomate-Mushroom Sauce or
Apple Butter. (See Dressings & Spreads.)

BLUEBERRIES BUCKLED

1 slice toast
2 oz. cottage cheese
sweetener as desired

1/4 cup blueberries, unsweetened, frozen or fresh

Slice toast to half its thickness to make two thin pieces
of toast. Put cottage cheese on a plate and smash it with
a fork until it's smooth. Fold in blueberries and sweetener.
Spread on two pieces of toast. Heat thoroughly in oven.

16

As a breakfast, this equals your cottage cheese and 1/2 fruit serving. For lunch add 1 oz. cottage or tuna to your salad bowl so your serving equals 3 oz.

BREAD PUDDING (FOR BREAKFAST)

1 slice bread cut into 1/4
   inch cubes
1 cup skimmed milk
1 egg

dash of salt
1/2 teaspoon vanilla
sweetener, if desired

Put bread cubes into individual Pyrex cups. Scald the milk, beat the egg slightly then stir in the cooled milk, salt and vanilla. Put the baking cups in a pan of warm water and pour egg mixture over the bread cubes. Bake at 350 degrees for about 45 minutes. Serves 1.

This is good hot or cold but since it takes a while in the morning to prepare I like to make it after dinner and eat it cold in the morning.

BRAN MUFFINS

1 apple (4 oz.) peeled
1 slice whole wheat bread

1/4 teaspoon maple flavoring
1 egg
1 T. brown sugar substitute

Coarsely grate apple and set aside. In bowl, beat egg add sweetener and maple flavoring. Crumb bread in blender, add to egg mixture, mix well. Stir in grated apple. Spoon into muffin tins that have been sprayed with PAM. . Bake at 375 degrees for 40-45 minutes. Let cool in the pan before removing. Entire recipe equals: 1 bread, 1 egg, 1 fruit for breakfast. This is also delicious made with white enriched bread with cinnamon and nutmeg for flavoring.

"BUTTER" FOR MUFFINS

1 envelope unflavored gelatin
1/4 cup cold water
1/4 cup boiling water
1/2 teaspoon butter flavoring

2 t. dry milk powder
1/8 teaspoon salt
1 drop of yellow food
  coloring

Soften gelatin on cold water in small saucepan. Add boiling water, butter flavor, salt, food coloring and then the dry milk powder, stirring to dissolve. Pour into container, cover tightly and store in refrigerator. Dissolve small amounts in egg poacher as needed. May be used in SMALL amounts on muffins and cooked vegetables.

NUT PASTRY FOR BREAKFAST

1/3 cup dry milk powder
1 T. hot black coffee
1/4 teaspoon vanilla
    1 slice whole wheat bread, toasted.

sweetener to equal 1 1/4 t.
    sugar
1/4 t. toasted sesame seeds

Slice toast into two thin slices. Mix first four ingredients and spread on toast pieces. Sprinkle with sesame
seeds and place under broiler till brown and bubbly. This
equals 1 glass of milk and one slice of bread. Add the
rest of your breakfast (egg or choice of cheese and some
fruit.) This pastry could also be cut into fingers and
served at lunch provided your are not going to use milk
any other way today.

SWISS LORRAINE

Crust:
4 slices bread, toasted and
   crumbed in blender
1/3 cup cold water

1 t. vanilla
sweetener to equal 2 T. sugar

Combine liquids and stir into bread crumbs in a pie plate.
Lightly press onto bottom and sides with a wet fork. Bake
at 400 degrees for 10 minutes or until crust is lightly
browned. Cool.

Filling:
1/2 cup chopped onions
1 cup water
1/3 cup dry milk powder

2 eggs, lightly beaten
2 oz. Swiss cheese, grated
1 cup liquid skimmed milk

Cook onions in water until tender. Add milk powder.
Pour into slightly beaten eggs, stirring briskly, and return
to heat. Add the liquid skimmed milk, cheese, salt and
pepper and heat through. Pour into pie shell and bake at 400
degrees for 20 minutes. You can arrange asparagus spears in
crust if you don't care for onions, and pour filling over
them and bake. Entire recipe serves 4 for breakfast. Do
try this - it's delicious.

LUNCHES

TUNA LUNCHEON SURPRISE

1 slice white bread, toasted
½ box frozen broccoli (½ bunch
   if fresh)
½ box frozen cauliflower
   (½ head if fresh)
1 small can drained mushrooms,
   sliced

3 oz. tuna fish
4 oz. skim milk
½ C. finely diced green
   pepper
Dehydrated onion flakes
Salt, pepper to taste

Put toast through blender to make bread crumbs. Combine
<u>cooked</u> broccoli and cauliflower in baking dish. Add tuna,
onions, and green pepper, folding gently so as not to mash
other vegetables. Put mushrooms, skim milk, salt and pepper through blender to make creamed mushroom sauce. Pour
over contents of baking dish. Sprinkle bread crumbs on
top and bake for 30 minutes in 350° oven.

This recipe serves ONE, with 1/2 C. milk.

SHRIMP PATRICE

3 oz. cooked, cold shrimp
Lettuce
Radishes
Dehydrated onion flakes
¼ t. lemon juice

Parsley
1 cucumber
Pimiento strips
CAPE COD DRESSING (see
   Dressings & Spreads)

Dice very fine the cucumber and add onion flakes, parsley,
lemon juice, and shrimp cut into large pieces. Place on a
bed of lettuce and garnish with radishes and pimiento.
Pour Cape Cod Dressing generously. Serves 1. (Don't forget your bread.)

SLOPPY JOE TUNA

4 oz. Zippy Zero (see Dressings
   & Spreads)
1 small green onion, minced

½ C. diced celery
3 oz. tuna

Heat Zippy Zero, add onion and celery and simmer briefly.
(Don't cook out all the crunch.) Add tuna, heat and
serve on toast. Serves 1.

OYSTER STEW

3 oz. oysters
1 C. skim milk

Salt, pepper
Drop of yellow food
   coloring

Heat the skim milk, add oysters, and heat until the edges
start to curl. Add food coloring, salt and pepper. Dehydrated onion flakes and mushroom bits are good too. Also
a dash of Worcestershire Sauce may be added. Pour into a
bowl and garnish with a dash of paprika, or chopped green
onion tops. Serves 1, with 1 C. milk. Melba Toasties are
good with this.

CRUNCHIN LUNCHEON

3 oz. cottage cheese
1 T. buttermilk or skim milk

½ t. lemon juice
Dash of salt

Put all in blender and whip until smooth. Use as a dip for
any vegetables or combinations such as carrot strips, radish
discs, cauliflowerettes, cucumber quarters, green pepper
strips, etc. Entire recipe equals 1 serving of cottage
cheese for lunch. This is a good substitute for sour cream,
but does not withstand heating or cooking.

Curry Dip--add 1/2 t. curry powder and 1 t. horseradish
Chili Dip--add 2 T. of our Ketchip (see Dressings & Spreads)
Wild and Wooly--add 2 T. soy sauce and 1/2 t. garlic salt
Mint Dip for fruit--1 T. fresh mint leaves and dash of
     sweetener
Pimiento Dip--add 2 t. drained, chopped pimiento
California Dip--add 1 t. instant beef bouillon powder and
     1 t. dehydrated onion flakes. Let flavors blend for
     1 hour before serving.

CHICKEN AND DRESSING

3 oz. cooked chicken breast
4 oz. can mushroom pieces, drained
1 piece bread, toasted and crumbed
    in blender

½ C. skim milk
1 T. parsley
Dash of garlic powder
½ t. poultry seasoning
Paprika

Combine all ingredients, reserving a few bread crumbs.
Place in attractive small baking dish, top with the re-
served crumbs and paprika. Bake 425° for 35 minutes.
Deduct milk from daily allowance. Serves 1.

STRAWBERRY PIE

Follow recipe for breakfast, but increase cottage cheese
to 12 oz. total. Or instead of increasing cottage cheese,
have a tossed salad with 1 oz. seafood or chicken sprinkled
on top.

COTTAGE CHEESE ASPIC

1 envelope gelatin
½ C. water
2 beef bouillon cubes
1½ C. tomato juice

1 t. dry onion flakes
1 t. horseradish
½ t. Worcestershire Sauce
9 oz. cottage cheese

Sprinkle gelatin on water to soften. Add bouillon cubes and stir over low heat until cubes are dissolved. Remove from heat and add juice and seasonings. Chill until syrupy and fold in cottage cheese. Chill until firm. Serves 3.

CLAM CHOWDER

6 oz. clams
½ C. green pepper, diced
½ C. green onion, diced tops
   and all
½ C. chopped celery

1 C. tomato juice
1 C. water
¼ C. grated carrots
1 t. dried thyme
Salt and pepper

Drain clams, and put juice and all other ingredients except clams in saucepan and simmer half an hour. Add clams. Serves 2. A tossed salad and Melba Toasties round out a filling meal.

CHEERY TUNA SALAD

6 oz. tuna
1 C. cherry tomatoes, halved
½ C. diced green onion
½ C. diced celery
Cucumber, if desired
¼ C. cider vinegar

¼ C. water
1 t. marjoram
Sweetener to taste, if
   desired
Salt and pepper
4 C. shredded lettuce

Combine tuna, tomatoes, onions, and celery. Toss with the dressing made with the remaining ingredients and serve on a bed of shredded lettuce. Serves 2 for lunch with 1 fruit each.

CHICKEN A LA KING ON BROCCOLI

1 chicken bouillon cube
1 C. water
1 T. dry onion flakes
1 T. dry pepper flakes
Dash of cloves

2½ T. dry milk powder
2 slices bread
6 oz. diced cooked
   chicken
2 T. pimiento
1 package frozen broc-
   coli spears, cooked

Cook bouillon cube, water, onion flakes, pepper flakes, and cloves together for 5 minutes. Put in blender and add dry milk powder and bread slices torn into several pieces. Blend for 10 seconds. Return to pan, add chicken and pimiento, and heat through. Serve over broccoli. Serves 2 for lunch and includes bread and chicken allowance and 1/4 cup milk for each person.

CHICKEN "NOODLE" SOUP

2 C. chicken bouillon
1 can bean sprouts, drained
1/2 t. dry onion flakes

1/2 t. dry red bell pepper
    flakes
1/2 t. celery salt
3 oz. cooked chicken

Simmer drained, washed bean sprouts and spices together in bouillon for 20 minutes. Add chicken and cook for another 10 minutes. Good with Melba Toasties. This equals 1 lunch portion. The possibilities of additional herbs and spices are limited only to your imagination. You may also use diced turkey instead of chicken.

JELLIED CHICKEN

1 envelope gelatin
1½ C. chicken bouillon
1/2 C. LoMaize (see Dressings &
    Spreads)

6 oz. cooked chicken
1/2 C. diced celery
1 T. minced green onion
    tops
1/4 C. grated carrots

Sprinkle gelatin over 1/2 C. bouillon in small saucepan. Place over low heat to dissolve gelatin. Add other cup of bouillon and cool. Add LoMaize and chill until it starts to thicken. Fold in chicken, celery, onion tops, and carrots. Chill until firm. Serve with fingers of toast, 3 or 4 to a piece of bread. Serves 2 for lunch, but you could double it easily to serve your bridge foursome.

COTTAGE CHEESE SOUFFLE SALAD

1 envelope unflavored gelatin
1/2 C. cold water
3/4 C. ice water
2 T. lemon juice
1/2 C. LoMaize

12 oz. cottage cheese
1 C. chopped raw spinach
1/2 C. minced celery
1 T. minced green onion
    tops

Soften gelatin on cold water and heat to dissolve. Add ice water, lemon juice, and LoMaize. Blend well. Chill until syrupy and then beat with mixer until fluffy. Fold in remaining ingredients. Chill in refrigerator. Serve on lettuce cups. Serves 4. Don't forget your bread.

BLENDED CHICKEN SALAD

6 oz. cooked chicken
1/4 C. LoMaize
1/4 C. green pepper, in chunks

1 stalk celery, sliced
1 whole pimiento

Place all but chicken in blender container. Mix at low
speed about 20 seconds. Turn into serving bowl, add chicken
and toss together. Serves 2 very generously. Don't forget
bread.

CHEAPIE-QUICKIE

1 # can mackerel	1 t. dry red or green
1 package unflavored gelatin	pepper flakes
1/2 C. water	1 T. capers (optional)
1 t. dry onion flakes	2 T. lemon juice
	1/2 C. minced celery

Drain mackerel, and add enough water to liquid to equal 1/2
cup. Sprinkle gelatin on mixture to soften. In a small
saucepan or skillet, mix 1/2 C. water with onion and pepper
flakes and bring to a boil. Add softened gelatin mixture
and stir until gelatin is dissolved. Put mackerel, capers,
and lemon juice in blender, add hot mixture and blend together 20 seconds. Remove from blender and stir in celery.
Spoon into 4 custard cups or molds and chill until firm.
Serve on lettuce. Serves 4. This can be made ahead of
time, like the day before, and keeps well enough to serve
2 people 2 lunches! (2 different days!)

SHRIMP COCKTAIL

1 package unflavored gelatin	1 T. Horseradish
1/2 C. water	Dash Tabasco
1 C. LoMaize	6 oz. cooked shrimp
1 C. Minor Thousand Island Dressing	

Sprinkle gelatin over water in saucepan. Heat slowly,
until gelatin dissolves. Cool. Stir in LoMaize, Minor
Thousand, horseradish, and Tabasco. Chill until syrupy,
and then fold in cooked, diced shrimp. Chill until firm.
Serves 2 gourmets.

SPICY SALMON

12 oz. canned salmon	1/2 t. peppercorns
1 C. vinegar	Dash of salt
1 t. whole cloves	1 bay leaf
1/2 t. whole allspice	

Drain salmon, and put in a shallow bowl. Make a marinade
of the remaining ingredients, bring to a boil, and pour
over the fish. Cover and let stand overnight. Drain and
serve in a lettuce cup, garnished with lemon slices,
cucumber strips, and green pepper rings. Serves 4.

TUNA CHOW MEIN

1 C. Zippy Zero (see Dressings & Spreads)
1 T. soy sauce
1/4 t. hot pepper flakes

1 can bean sprouts, drained
6 oz. tuna

Heat Zippy Zero, add bean sprouts, hot pepper flakes, soy sauce, and tuna. Heat through and serve on toast. Serves 2.

GREEN MOLD

1 envelope unflavored gelatin
1/2 C. cold water
2 T. lime juice
1 T. cider vinegar
1 T. horseradish
1 C. skim milk

12 oz. cottage cheese
1/2 C. minced celery
1/2 C. minced green pepper
1/4 C. minced green onion

Soften gelatin on cold water and heat to dissolve. Add lime juice, vinegar, and horseradish. Cool until thick, then stir in milk and cottage cheese. Chill until syrupy, and fold in vegetables. Spoon into 4 molds. When ready to serve, unmold on lettuce leaves and garnish with radish discs and cucumber slices. Serves 4. Deduct ¼ C. milk from your daily allowance.

TOSS-UP

6 oz. cooked chicken, diced
1 C. celery, sliced
1/2 C. cauliflowerettes, diced

2 T. chopped green peppers
2 green onions, minced
1/2 C. LoMaize, room temp.

Toss all ingredients together and serve on a lettuce cup. Serves TWO for lunch.

HALF-AND-HALF

3 oz. cold (leftover) fish, shredded
3 oz. cottage cheese
1 green onion, chopped
1 T. green pepper, minced

1/2 stalk celery, minced
1/2 C. bean sprouts
1 T. parsley
1/4 C. LoMaize

You won't believe how good this is until you try it.

Combine all ingredients and serve in a lettuce cup. Or use it as a sandwich spread with lettuce or cabbage leaves for a top! Serves 2.

TUNA LUNCHEON RING

2 envelopes unflavored gelatin
1/2 C. cold water
1-1/4 C. boiling water
1/4 C. lemon juice
1 t. onion salt

Ice water
12 oz. tuna, flaked
1 C. celery, minced
1/4 C. green pepper, diced
1 T. pimiento, minced

Soften gelatin on cold water. Add boiling water and stir to dissolve gelatin. Add lemon juice, onion salt, and enough ice water to bring total amount to 3-1/2 cups. If you use some ice cubes, it will begin to jell more quickly. When it starts to thicken, add remaining ingredients and turn into a rinsed ring mold. Chill. Serves 4 for lunch.

MARINATED TUNA FOR LUNCH

6 oz. drained tuna

2 T. lemon juice

Sprinkle tuna with lemon juice, then marinate in this sour cream:

3 oz cottage cheese
Dash of salt

1 T. buttermilk or skim milk

Toss them together and chill. Overnight chilling is best. This is a great change for lunch and a new way to serve tuna. Serve in lettuce cups with cucumber slices, if desired. Serves 3.

MULLIGATAWNEY SOUP

1/4 C. diced green onions
1/4 C. diced carrots
1/4 c. diced celery
1 green pepper, chopped fine
1 apple, diced large
8 oz. raw chicken, skinned and diced

1 C. tomato juice
1 t. curry powder
1/2 t. allspice
1 T. dried parsley
4 C. chicken bouillon, or chicken broth, de-fatted

Simmer all ingredients but the chicken bouillon together for about 45 minutes. Add the bouillon and heat to boiling. This equals two lunch servings with 1/2 fruit each.

FANCY FILLETS

2 slices bread, crumbed in blender
4 T. buttermilk

1 # frozen fillet of sole, thawed enough to separate

Put buttermilk in a pie plate, roll individual pieces of fish in it, then roll in bread crumbs. Place fillets on teflon baking pan or aluminum foil. Sprinkle with parsley, onion salt and herbs of your choice. Bake at 350° for 25 minutes or until fish flakes easily with a fork, and bread crumbs are brown. Serves four for lunch with 1/2 slice of bread each, and 1 T. milk.

CREAMED CHICKEN ON TOAST

10 oz. package of frozen
   cauliflower
3 oz. celery, minced
1 t. onion flakes
1 C. water

6 oz. cooked chicken
2 T. red or green peppers
2 T. green onion tops
2-1/2 T. dry milk powder

Cook cauliflower, celery and onion flakes in water until soft. Puree entire contents of pan until smooth, then return to saucepan. Add remaining ingredients, stirring milk powder in last. Heat through and serve on toast for lunch. Recipe serves 2 with 1/4 C. milk each.

SALMON STUFFED PEPPERS

4 medium sized green peppers
1/2 t. salt
1/4 C. finely chopped onions
1/4 C. finely chopped celery

1# can salmon, drained
1/4 C. zippy Zero Dressing
2 slices bread, crumbed in
   blender

Cut thin slice from top of pepper and remove seeds. Cook in boiling water with 1/2 t. salt for 5 minutes. Drain, then sprinkle inside of peppers with salt and pepper. Combine onion, celery, salmon, Zippy Zero and bread crumbs. Mix well. Stuff peppers, stand upright in baking dish and bake uncovered for 20 to 25 minutes at 350°. Serves 4 for lunch with 1/2 slice of bread each..

SHRIMP CREOLE

12 oz. cooked, cleaned shrimp
1 onion, sliced thin
1 stalk celery, diced
1 clove garlic, minced

1 small green pepper, minced
1/2 t. chili powder
1 C. tomato juice

Mix all ingredients except shrimp and cook until juice is only half the original volume. Add shrimp and simmer 15 minutes. Recipe serves 4 for lunch. Really delicious!

CLAM LUNCHEON

CLAM LUNCHEON:

1 can (8 oz.) minced clams	drop of Tabasco
1 package unflavored gelatin	1 t. dry green pepper flakes
1 C. skimmed milk	1 t. dry onion flakes
1/2 t. Worcestershire Sauce	about 4 1/2 oz. of cottage
1/2 t. salt	cheese

Drain clams, reserving 1/2 C. liquid. Sprinkle gelatin over clam liquid in small saucepan. Place over low heat, stirring until gelatin dissolves, about 3 minutes. Add skimmed milk, Worcestershire Sauce, salt, Tabasco. Weigh clams and add enough cottage cheese to bring total amount to 9 ounces. Add this mixture to your first mixture after it has been chilled and is thick. Turn into three molds and continue chilling until firm.

This serves 3 for lunch, with 1/3 C. milk each and 3 ounces clam-cheese. This is delicious, and if you were a fan of fried clams, here's to your clam buds!

POLYNESIAN SHRIMP

12 oz. cooked shrimp	1/4 C. Minor Thousand Island
1/2 C. green pepper--par- boiled 2 minutes	Dressing (see Dressings and Spreads)
1 C. crushed unsweetened pine- apple--drained	Dash of Worcestershire Sauce

Combine shrimp, peppers and pineapple. Toss lightly with dressing and Worcestershire Sauce. Chill well and serve on bed of lettuce. This serves four for lunch with 1/2 fruit per person.

BOOTHBAY CHOWDER

1 C. chopped cabbage	1/2 t. tarragon
2 stalks celery, diced	6 oz. leftover cooked fish
1 green pepper, diced	2 C. chicken bouillon
1 green onion, diced	1/2 C. tomato juice
1 small carrot, diced	

Combine all ingredients except fish and simmer about 10 minutes or until tender. Add fish, flaked into bits, and simmer another 5 minutes. Serves 2 for lunch. If you don't have leftover fish, tuna or shrimp will be very good. Lobster pieces are truly scrumptious!

CREAMED TUNA ON TOAST

4 oz. can mushrooms
2 1/2 T. dry milk powder
1 t. dry bell peppers

1 t. dry onion flakes
1 t. parsley flakes
3 oz. tuna

Place mushrooms and liquid in blender and add milk; blend.
Turn into small saucepan and add remaining ingredients.
Simmer until hot. Serve on toast. Serves 1 for lunch with
1/2 C. milk.

SCALLOPED OYSTERS

8 oz. oysters and juice
mushrooms, drained

1/3 C. dry milk powder
2 slices of bread, made into
crumbs

Combine oysters and their juice with mushrooms, any amount
desired, in shallow casserole. Sprinkle milk powder on top
and bake 450 degrees for 15 minutes. Stir in the milk powder
and sprinkle on the bread crumbs. Bake another 5 minutes
or until brown. Serves 2 for lunch with 1/2 C. milk each.

DINNERS

CHICKEN CACCIATORE SUPREME

1 3/4 # boneless chicken breasts, cut into large pieces
2 small green peppers--large dice
1 small clove garlic
2 stalks celery--fine dice
2 T. chopped pimiento
2 bay leaves
1 1/2 C. drained, sliced mushrooms
2 C. stewed tomatoes
Salt, pepper, thyme, parsley- (fresh or dried)
Dehydrated onion flakes
3 dashes of soy sauce

It's best to pre-cook chicken for about 30 minutes, either roasting or broiling. When taken from the oven, skin and pat off any grease. The rest of the ingredients should be simmering very slowly in a saucepan for 30 minutes or until celery and pepper are soft.

Combine chicken and sauce and simmer together for about 20-30 minutes. If you wish a thicker sauce, uncover and simmer until sauce is reduced to desired thickness. Simmer very slowly. This recipe serves four with one fruit per serving.

HOT OR COLD FISH STEAK

7 oz. fresh or frozen fish steaks
Lemon juice
Soy sauce
Salt, pepper, parsley flakes
Dehydrated onion flakes
Sliced mushrooms

Place fish in shallow baking dish and brush with lemon juice. Add onion, salt, pepper, and parsley flakes. Sprinkle soy sauce liberally and cover the fish with mushrooms. If you use fresh mushrooms, slice them rather thick. Bake at 400 degrees for approximately 25-30 minutes. Serves 1.

This is very tasty served hot but for a change, try cutting the cooked steaks into cubes and serve ice cold. This makes a very special buffet dish and delicious picnic fare.

LAMB IN FOIL

Place 2 lamb chops, with all the fat cut off, in a roomy envelope of aluminum foil. Add:

1/4 onion, thinly sliced
1/2 tomato
1/2 green pepper, cut to desired size
garlic salt or powder
powdered basil leaves
salt, pepper

Fold tightly so no steam escapes. Place on baking sheet and bake for 1 hour at 350 degrees. Serves one. Equals 1 dinner portion meat and 1/2 fruit (tomato).

FLOUNDER NEW ORLEANS

4 oz. flounder fillet
3 oz. shrimp, scallops, and
  canned clams-cut fine
1/4 C. water
1/2 t. lemon juice
1/4 C. skim milk
nutmeg

several large mushrooms, cut
  any desired size
salt, pepper
dehydrated onion flakes
1 T. very finely minced green
  pepper
paprika

Put water, lemon juice, mushrooms, dehydrated onion flakes
and green pepper into shallow skillet and bring to a slow
simmer. Place fillet in liquid, cover and poach for about
5 minutes or until fillet loses its raw look. Remove fillet
and set aside.

Add skim milk to liquid in skillet and let simmer uncovered
until liquid boils down to about half volume. Now add shrimp,
scallops, and clams. Heat gently for about 2 minutes. Add
salt, pepper and paprika with just a dash of nutmeg. Place
fillet in oven proof serving dish and pour mixture over it.
Place high under broiler and brown for about 2 minutes.

This equals 5 oz. cooked fish and 1/4 C. skim milk.

CHICKEN "WHATCHAMACALLIT"

This is one of the easiest to prepare. So convenient if you
are the only one in your family dieting. Just take your
portion out and let your family devour the rest. Believe
me they will!

Chicken, without skin
Dehydrated onion flakes
Sliced carrots
Garlic powder

Sliced peppers
Whole mushrooms
Salt, pepper, paprika,
dash of soy sauce

Add one, two, or all of the following as you wish:

    cauliflower
    broccoli
    wax beans
    string beans

    cabbage
    celery
    eggplant
    asparagus

Arrange everything in a large baking pan with tight cover, or
cover with foil, but let no steam escape. Add just a little
bit of water to cover the bottom of the pan. Season all
ingredients and add soy sauce. Bake at 375 degrees for about
1 and 3/4 hours. The steam seals in the various flavors and
therefore it is very important to cover tightly.

The beauty of this is that you can try anything--veal, lamb,
beef, and any kind of vegetable you wish. You can also experiment with herbs such as dill or rosemary, but remember
a little goes a long way when steamed.

BEEF SAUERBRATEN

1 3/4 # round steak
1/2 t. onion salt
1/8 t. pepper
1/2 t. dry mustard

1 can (13 oz.) sauerkraut
with juice
1 C. tomato juice
1 t. Worcestershire sauce

Broil beef until brown. Combine other ingredients in a Dutch
Oven, skillet, or stew pot. Add beef. Simmer, covered, until
tender--about 1 1/2 hours. Serves four. This beef is tender
every time and makes a great company dish.

MILK-FED CHICKEN

1 1/2 # chicken breasts
2 C. buttermilk
2 T. lemon juice
2 t. salt

1/2 t. Tabasco
1 t. ground coriander
(if you have it)
1 t. paprika

Split chicken breasts in half. Mix other ingredients together, and marinate chicken pieces overnight. A heavy plastic
bag works fine. Drain very well. Broil in a hot broiler 15
minutes each side, or until tender. The outside will be
crispy and the inside very moist and delicious. The entire
recipe serves THREE with about 2 T. buttermilk each, so
deduct milk from daily allowance.

CURRIED LAMB

1 1/4 # cooked lamb, cubed
2 C. diced celery
1 C. diced carrots
1 t. Worcestershire Sauce
1 1/2 t. curry powder

2 C. chicken bouillon or
skimmed lamb broth
1 T. dry onion
1 t. salt

Combine all but the lamb and cook until vegetables are fork
tender. Add lamb and heat thoroughly. Serves FOUR.

PEPPER STEAK

1 3/4 # round steak
8 oz. can of tomatoes
1 1/2 C. water
1 T. dry onion flakes

1 clove garlic, minced
2 large green peppers,
in strips
1 package frozen French-
style green beans
1 1/2 t. Worcestershire

Brown steak in broiler and cut into strips. Remove to a Dutch
Oven and add tomatoes, water, onions, and garlic. Cover and
simmer for about 1 hour or until steak is tender. Stir in
remaining ingredients, Cover and simmer 5 minutes more. Serves
FOUR.

By THE RIGHT FLANK, MARCH!

7 oz. flank steak
4 T. soy sauce
2 T. water

1/2 t. dry onion flakes
1 T. dry parsley flakes

Make a marinade of the last four ingredients; pour over steak
and let set at room temperature for 2 hours, turning often.
Broil about 3 inches from heat about 3 minutes each side.
Serves ONE.

SPICY BEEF LIVER

1 3/4 # beef liver
8 oz. tomato juice
1 T. horseradish

1 t. lemon juice
1/2 t. parsley
1 T. minced dry onion flakes

Cut beef liver into strips about 1/2" wide and 3 " long. Brown
in Dutch oven or teflon pan. Simmer together remaining
ingredients and pour over the liver. The liver cooks very
quickly--and if overcooked can be very tough, so about 5
minutes after you add the sauce, the meat is done. This is
delicious even for people who are only so-so about liver.
The recipe equals FOUR dinner portions.

CHICKEN LITTLE

2 broiler-fryers, quartered
2 t. salt
1/2 C. salad mustard
2 T. Vinegar

2 T. water
1 t. thyme
1/4 t. ginger

Skin chicken and sprinkle with salt. Place in shallow baking
pan. Mix all the other ingredients, spoon onto chicken
and bake at 375 degrees about 1 hour. This recipe serves
FOUR but because of the various weights of fryers, weigh your
5 oz. dinner portion.

VEAL VIENNESE

2 or 3 carrots
thinly sliced veal (7 oz)
garlic powder
paprika, parsley

1 can mushrooms, sliced
1 green pepper, diced
1/2 C. tomato juice
skewers or thread

Peel carrots and cut in half lengthwise if thick. Season
veal on both sides with garlic powder, paprika and parsley.
In the center of veal slice put carrot stick and top with
mushrooms and green pepper. Roll veal around vegetables,
allowing carrot ends to extend. Skewer or tie with thread.
Place in roasting pan, pouring tomato juice over them.
Cover and roast at 350 degrees for one hour. Serves ONE.

MARY'S PATIO CHICKEN

Skin a broiler chicken and place in shallow baking pan or
on the grill. Mix ingredients and brush both sides of
chicken. Bake at 350 degrees for 1 hour, basting when you
think of it. Weigh your portion, because broilers vary in
size.

1/2 C. boiling water
3 chicken bouillon cubes
1 t. dry mustard
2 t. soy sauce
1/2 t. paprika

1 t. oregano
2 t. curry powder
2 dashes Tabasco
1 t. ginger
1 clove minced garlic
1 t. dry onion flakes

STUFFED PEPPERS

14 oz. lean ground beef
1/2# cooked mushrooms,
  cut small
6 green peppers, medium sized
8 oz. tomato juice
Salt, pepper

Garlic powder
Dehydrated (dry) onion flakes
1 T. parsley
1/2 t. celery salt
1/8 t. sage

Mix all ingredients except tomato juice and peppers in a
bowl. You may wish to add a little water to make mixture
easier to handle. Divide into 6 equal parts.

Wash peppers and remove tops and seeds. Soften by dropping
into boiling water for about 5 minutes. Remove and fill with
meat mixture and place in a shallow baking dish. Pour tomato
juice over peppers and bake until tender--about 25-30 minutes.
You may use as much or as little tomato juice as you wish on
the peppers. If you place the peppers fairly close together
in a small dish, you can take full advantage of the amount of
juice you are able to use. You may also use a beef bouillon
cube dissolved in water for sauce instead of tomato juice.

Three stuffed peppers equal your dinner portion of meat. Happy
feasting!

FILLET OF SOLE BAKE

7 oz. fillet of sole
soy sauce
dehydrated onion flakes
lemon juice

parsley flakes
garlic powder
salt, pepper, paprika

Place fish in baking dish and brush with lemon juice. Sprinkle
on some onion, parsley, garlic powder, salt, pepper, and
paprika according to your taste.

The soy sauce goes on last--use it liberally since it tends
to evaporate in the heat rather quickly. Bake at 375 degrees
for approximately 25 minutes.

Garnish with a thin slice of lemon and/or fresh parsley or
pimiento strips. This equals 5 oz. cooked fish (one dinner
portion.)

SWEET AND SOUR FISH

1 # flounder, sole or haddock (partially thawed and cut into
   4 squares.)

Combine in a large frying pan:

2 C. water
1 bay leaf
1 T. dehydrated onion flakes
Salt, pepper
dash of oregano
paprika
artificial sweetener to taste

2 whole cloves
dash of celery salt
1/2 t. vegetable flakes
   (or green pepper and
   celery flakes)
1 or 2 t. lemon juice
   (to taste)

Bring all ingredients to a boil and then add fish squares.
Simmer _very_ slowly for approximately 15 minutes. Baste often.
Chill and serve, measuring your portion for 5 oz.

FAR EAST INDIA STEW

4 oz. sliced onions
2 cloves garlic
2 T. curry powder

1 t. salt
2-1/2# chicken (skinned)
1 C. chicken bouillon

Heat the onions in non-stick fry pan or heavy Dutch oven.
Add garlic, curry powder and salt. Add the chicken pieces
and stir until they are nicely covered with the powder and
onions. Add bouillon and cook over low heat about 45
chicken pieces and rapidly cook down sauce to pour over
chicken. This recipe equals FOUR portions.

JAMAICAN GINGER CHICKEN

To 4 C. chicken bouillon or broth (after skimming) add:

1 t. onion salt
1 T. ground coriander
1 t. crushed hot red pepper
1 t. curry powder
1 C. carrots

1/2 t. garlic powder
1 t. crushed caraway seed
1 t. ground ginger
4 C. slant cut celery

Simmer until barely tender, then add:

1 1/4 # cooked chicken--
 bite sized pieces
4 oz. can mushrooms

2 T. soy sauce
2 cans bean sprouts, drained

Reheat and enjoy. One quarter of entire recipe equals one
meat portion. This dish is hot and spicy. No bland
chicken here!

SHRIMP KONA KAIA

1 medium green pepper, cut
 into 1" pieces
1/3 C. water
1/2 C. unsweetened pineapple
 juice
10 oz. cooked shrimp

1/2 C. pineapple chunks
 cut canned chunks in 1/2
 again
2 t. lemon juice
1 T. soy sauce
a pinch of crushed ginger,
 if desired

Cook green pepper in water until tender. Remove from heat
and add juices, soy sauce, and pineapple. Cook until
thickened, stirring constantly. Add shrimp. Heat and
serve. This makes a wonderful buffet dish. Try serving it
over bean sprouts for a "chop suey" effect.

Serves two. 1/2 of the total equals 1 dinner portion
shrimp and 1 fruit.

JELLIED LIVER PATE

1 # chicken livers
1 T. dry onion
1/2 clove peeled garlic
1/2 bay leaf
2 C. chicken bouillon

1 small can mushrooms,
 drained
Salt and pepper
1 T. unflavored gelatin
1/3 C. white vinegar mixed
 with 2 T. lemon juice

Simmer first four ingredients with 1 c. of the bouillon for
20 minutes. Remove bay leaf. Cool. Put solids and 1 C.
liquid through blender. Add mushrooms, salt, pepper, and
puree until smooth. Soften gelatin in vinegar mix, in
bowl. Heat the second cup of bouillon to boiling and add to
the gelatin, stirring until it is dissolved. Then add the
blender contents and mix thoroughly. Pour into mold or loaf
pan and chill until set. This equals 3 dinner portions, but
you could use an eighth of it for an appetizer and have 3
oz. of some other meat for the rest of your dinner portion!

BOUILLABAISSE
(The best this side of New Orleans)

1 can lobster meat (5 oz.)
1 can clams (8 oz.)
8 oz. cooked shrimp
1 # fish--a combination of
  perch, haddock, cod, etc.
3 T. dry onion
2 cloves garlic, finely chopped
8 oz. tomato juice

1/2 t. thyme
1 T. parsley
1 bay leaf
1 strip of orange
  rind
1 T. salt
1/4 t. pepper
1 quart boiling water or
  fish stock

Cut perch and/or other fish into 1 1/2 inch cubes. Heat tomato juice, add lobster meat, shrimp, fish, onion and garlic. Simmer about 10 minutes. Add remaining ingredients and simmer over low heat about 30 minutes. Makes 6 dinner portions. A very impressive dish!

WHOLLY MACKEREL

1 can mackerel, drained
  (about 10 oz.)
2 T. dry onion flakes

3/4 C. finely chopped celery
1/2 T. lemon juice
2 T. salad mustard

Flake the well-drained mackerel. Add onion, celery, lemon juice, and mustard. Shape into patties and bake 20 minutes at 350 degrees. Makes 4 good-sized patties, and serves two for dinner.

Many people like this made with salmon, too.

SEAFOOD VALENCIA

1/4 t. orange extract
1 C. water
2 T. pickling spice

1/2 t. salt
1 3/4 # fish

Combine all but the fish in a large skillet. Heat but do not boil. Add fish, cover and simmer for 10 minutes. This recipe serves FOUR for dinner. You may also broil or bake the fish but keep basting with the sauce. This is a very unusual and tasty dish.

SAMPAN PATTIES

1 small onion, diced
1 3/4 Lbs. ground round
1/2 C. tomato juice or
  Zippy Zero Dressing
1/2 green pepper, minced

4 oz. can drained mushrooms,
  bits and pieces
1 can bean sprouts, well
  drained

Combine and shape into patties and broil. Entire recipe
equals 4 dinner portions of beef. This is especially
good on the grill.

HUNGARIAN GOULASH

7 oz. stewing beef	2 beef bouillon cubes
4 oz. carrots	1 1/2 C. water
1/2 can French style green	1 T. soy sauce
beans	oregano
1/2 can sliced mushrooms	dehydrated onion flakes
1 green pepper, diced	garlic powder
1/2 can bean sprouts	salt, pepper

Drain all vegetables, mix all ingredients except bean
sprouts and cook until meat and carrots are tender (about
1 1/2 hours.) Add drained bean sprouts about 10 minutes
before removing from flame. This entire recipe equals one
dinner portion.

FISH EN FRUIT

1# frozen perch, cod, etc.   4 oz. grapefruit juice

Place fish in baking dish. Add the grapefruit juice, cover
with foil, and bake 350° about 1 hour, or until the fish flakes.
It has a delicious sweet-sour taste, and couldn't be simpler
to prepare. If your fish is thawed, it can also be poached
in a skillet on the burner, but don't overcook. Five to ten
minutes is enough. Your portion is 5 oz. cooked and the entire recipe has 1 fruit portion.

BRAISED LIVER

1/2 C. water	1 beef bouillon cube .
7 oz. beef or chicken livers	1 T. onion flakes

Combine water and bouillon cube, simmer for five minutes.
Add liver, cover with onion flakes, reduce heat and let
simmer until liquid is reduced to half. Turn, and let
simmer down until nearly dry; turn, so that both sides are
browned and flavored with condensed liquid.

Serves one very tastefully!

BROILED FILLETS WITH HERBS

14 oz. red snapper fillets	2 T. fresh chives
2 t. lemon juice	1 T. dried parsley
1 1/2 t. salt	1/2 t. dried tarragon
1 t. paprika	1/2 t. ginger

Sprinkle lemon juice over fillets and add mixture of
remaining ingredients. To broil fillets: Broil 4 "
from heat for 10 minutes per inch of thickness. If you
use frozen fillets, double the cooking time. Serves 2.

SKILLET FISH

1/2 C. tomato juice	1/2 t. salt
1/2 C. chopped onion	1/2 t. oregano
3 T. chopped green pepper	1 # flounder fillets
1 T. dried parsley	

Cook all but fish together for 5 minutes. Add fish and
simmer gently until fish will flake with a fork, about 5
to 10 minutes, depending on thickness of fillets. Your
allowance for dinner is 5 oz. cooked fish.

BROILED CHICKEN

2-1/2 Lb. broiler, skinned   Marinade for chicken or
                                fish (see dressings/spreads)

Simmer marinade for 2 minutes then spread on chicken and let
set at room temperature for 1/2 hour before broiling. Broil
chicken for 30 minutes, turn and baste with any marinade that
may be left in mixing bowl. Broil until light brown and
tender, about 15-20 minutes more. Your Slim and Trim portion
is 5 oz. cooked chicken.

SEASONED CHICKEN

2-1/2 Lb. broiler, skinned   Seasoned Salt (see dress-
                                ings and Spreads)

Place skinned, cut-up chicken in baking pan. Cover with
a tight fitting lid, or aluminum foil. Bake 350 degrees for
45 minutes. Drain broth into a jar to skim and save for
another day. Return drained chicken to oven, uncovered, and
sprinkle with seasoned salt, and bake for another 15-20
minutes, or until it's dry and crisp. Your Slim and Trim
portion is 5 oz. cooked meat.

VEAL PAPRISH

7 oz. cubed veal	1/4 t. caraway seeds
1 small onion, peeled and diced	Salt, pepper
1 clove garlic, minced	1/4 C. water
1 t. paprika	1/4 C. buttermilk

Toss onion and garlic together and stir in a Dutch oven or
Teflon skillet. Brown the meat with the onion and garlic,
and add all other ingredients except the buttermilk.
Cover and simmer over low heat until tender. Remove from

heat and pour the buttermilk over the meat. Heat but do not let it boil. Serves 1 meat portion for dinner, and don't forget to deduct buttermilk from your milk allowance for the day.

ROAST LEG OF LAMB

6 lb. leg of lamb
2 t. salt
1 t. dried thyme leaves
1/2 t. pepper
2 celery stalks, sliced

2 t. dry onion flakes
2 C. chicken bouillon
  with 3 T. lemon juice
  added
1 T. dried tarragon
  leaves

Rub lamb with salt, pepper, and thyme. Put sliced celery and dry onion in roasting pan. Place lamb on top. Pour 1 C. bouillon over. Roast, uncovered, in 325° oven, basting occasionally, for 3 hours. Bring other cup of bouillon and tarragon leaves to a boil. Strain pan drippings into 2 cup measure, pour off all fat. Add water if necessary to make 1 cup of remaining liquid. Return to roasting pan, add tarragon mix, and bring to a boil. Serve over lamb. Slim and Trim allowance is 5 oz. cooked lamb.

To freeze leftover lamb, slice and remove all fat. Cover with leftover sauce or mint sauce from Dressings/Spreads section and this way you can easily have 5 oz. of lamb anytime you wish.

CHICKEN HAVAHI

9 oz. breast of chicken, skinned
1/2 C. chunk pineapple with juice
  (unsweetened)

1 T. lemon juice
2 t. soy sauce

Place chicken in shallow dish. Drain juice from chunks and mix with lemon juice and soy sauce. Brush on chicken and bake, uncovered, in a 400° oven for 45 minutes, basting two or three times with the sauce. Place chunk pineapple around chicken and bake another 5 minutes to heat the chunks. This recipe equals 1 meat and 1 fruit serving.

TACO TEASER

14 oz. ground round
1/4 c. chopped onion
1 lb. can green beans
1/2 C. Ketchip (see Dressings/
  Spreads)

1/2 C. liquid from the
  beans
1 T. chili powder
4 C. shredded lettuce
1/2 C. sliced green
  onions

Broil meat until done; remove to a skillet, and fork meat into small bits. Add onions, beans, Ketchip, liquid, and chili powder. Simmer 15 minutes. Combine lettuce and green onion in individual salad bowls. Add meat sauce and toss together lightly. Serves 2 for dinner.

ORIENTAL LAMB CHOPS

2 lamb chops (about 9 oz.)
1/2 C. soy sauce
1/2 C. water

1 clove garlic, minced
1/4 t. ground ginger

Mix together the soy sauce, water, garlic, and ginger. Marinate the lamb chops in it for several hours. Broil the chops for 10 minutes, turn, and broil the other side 5 to 8 minutes more. Serves one.

VEAL STEW

7 oz. stewing veal, cubed
1 small onion, sliced
1/2 C. Zippy Zero

1 small can mushrooms, drained
1 small carrot, sliced

Brown veal and onions in Dutch oven or Teflon skillet. Stir in Zippy Zero, cover and cook for 30 minutes. Add mushrooms and carrot and cook 30 minutes longer. If more liquid is needed, use the liquid from the mushrooms. Serves one for dinner.

BUCKINGHAM SOLE

14 oz. fillet of sole
1 medium onion
1/2 C. white vinegar with 2 T.
    lemon juice added
2 tomatoes

1/2 C. green peppers, chopped
1/2 C. green onions, chopped
1/4 t. Tabasco
1/4 t. Worcestershire sauce

Place fish in a shallow baking dish and cover with thin slices of onion. Cover with marinade of vinegar and lemon juice and marinate in refrigerator 24 hours. Peel tomatoes, drain the marinade from the fish, reserving 1/4 cup, and put tomato slices on the fish. Toss on the green peppers and onions, and stir the Tabasco and Worcestershire in the reserved marinade. Use this to baste occasionally. Bake 375° for 25 minutes or until it flakes. Serves 2 with 1 fruit each.

CHICAGO SALAD

5 oz. cold roast beef
1 onion, thinly sliced
1/2 C. LoMaize (see Dressings/ Spreads)

1 t. curry powder
1 T. prepared mustard
2 C. shredded lettuce

Cut roast beef into julienne strips and mix with the onion. Mix together the LoMaize, curry powder and mustard. Toss with beef and onion. If you're in no particular rush, or you are one of those people who plan ahead, let this mixture marinate in the refrigerator for 3 or 4 hours. Serve atop the lettuce bed, and garnish with green pepper strips and radishes.

BARBEQUED SPARERIBS

9 oz. beef spareribs
1/2 C. Chicken Bar-B-Q Sauce (see Dressings/Spreads)

Cover spareribs with cold water and bring to a boil. Simmer for one hour. Remove from water, cut into individual ribs and place in roasting pan. Cover with Bar-B-Q sauce and bake in 350° oven for 15 minutes; turn, baste and bake 10 minutes longer. Truly scrumptious with a tossed salad and lots of paper napkins!

CHILI TOMORROW

6 C. water
2 beef bouillon cubes
1-3/4 lbs. ground round
1/2 C. chopped onion
1/2 C. diced green peppers
4 C. diced celery
1-1/2 C. tomato juice

1-1/2 t. salt
2 t. paprika
1 t. oregano
1 T. chili powder
2 cloves garlic, minced
2 cans French-Style green beans

Bring to a boil the water, boiillon cubes and ground round. Simmer for 15 minutes. Remove from heat and chill well, so you can skim off all the fat. Then return to the stove, add all but the green beans and simmer for one hour. Just before serving, add the beans, undrained if you like, and heat through. Serves four for dinner.

STUFFED ROCK CORNISH HEN

1 Rock Cornish hen about 18 oz.
1 can drained bean sprouts
1/2 C. chopped celery
1/2 C. grated carrot
1 T. dry onion flakes

1 t. sage or poultry seasoning
1 T. soy sauce
1 T. lemon juice

Make a stuffing of the list of ingredients above, and stuff the bird, after wiping it inside and out with paper towels. Stuff neck opening as well as body, and tie or skewer legs together. Put on rack and roast uncovered in 350° oven about one hour, until tender and golden. Serves 2 for dinner with or without candle light.

POACHED SALMON IN COURT BOUILLON

14 oz. salmon steak
Court Bouillon as follows:
1 quart boiling water
3 chicken bouillon cubes
2 T. white vinegar

1 small onion, sliced
1 bay leaf
2" piece of yellow
 lemon peel
Salt and pepper

Simmer the court bouillon for 1/2 hour. Strain. Carefully place salmon in liquid, using cheese cloth around it for easy removal if desired. Simmer salmon for 8 minutes, or until it flakes easily with a fork. Serves two. To serve cold, let it chill in the liquid. Garnish with lemon wedges, serve with Cucumber Dressing if desired.

BEEF AND CABBAGE

14 oz. cube steak
2 C. water
1 T. chopped onion
1 beef bouillon cube

2 carrots
1 small head cabbage,
 quartered

Cut cube steak in strips. Put in heavy kettle and brown. Drain off fat. Add water, onion, bouillon cube and simmer for one hour. Slice the carrots in thin pennies and add with the cabbage to the meat. Cover and simmer one hour. Serves TWO.

MARINATED STEAK

9 oz. rib steak (or any cut you wish)
1/2 C. soy sauce
2 t. ground ginger
1 clove garlic, diced

Marinate steak for one hour in above mixture, at room temperature. Broil about 10 minutes, turn and broil 8 minutes more. Serves 1 for dinner.

HERB BAKED CHICKEN

2-1/4 lb. chicken, skinned and
 cut into serving pieces
4 carrots, scraped, and halved
 into 1" pieces

1 onion, chunked
2 large celery stalks,
 cut into 3" lengths
1 chicken bouillon cube

1/2 C. boiling water   1 T. parsley
1 t. basil   1/4 t. thyme

Place carrots, onion and celery in 8" square baking dish.
Dissolve bouillon cube in boiling water, add herbs. Cover
vegetables with chicken pieces, cover with bouillon sauce
and bake, tightly covered for 1-1/2 hours. Remove cover
last 15 minutes to brown chicken. Sprinkle with a bit
more parsley and serve. Weigh out your 5 oz. portion.
Serves 4 for dinner.

JUST FOR THE HALIBUT

1 C. chicken bouillon   1 carrot, sliced into
1 onion, thinly sliced   pennies
1 t. dry pepper flakes   7 oz. halibut or any
                              other fish you wish

Simmer first four ingredients together in a tightly covered
skillet until tender. Place fish on top of the vegetables
and sprinkle with a dash of parsley and paprika. Simmer
until fish is fork tender--about 10 minutes. This equals
1 dinner portion.

MEAT BALLS WITH SAUCE

14 oz. ground round   1 t. oregano
1 C. Zippy Zero (see Dressings   1 T. Worcestershire
   and Spreads)   sauce
1 t. basil   2 cloves garlic, if
                              desired

Make ground round into thirty small meat balls. Brown
until done in broiler. Combine remaining ingredients and
boil--then simmer. Add meat balls and simmer again for
30 minutes. Serves 2 for dinner. This is also good
served over drained, chopped, heated, bean sprouts.

SIMPLY CHICKEN

2 1/2# chicken pieces   2 cloves garlic,
1/2 C. grapefruit or orange juice   minced

Skin chicken and place in shallow casserole. Pour on the
juice and garlic, cover tightly and bake at 350° for about
1¼ hours. Remove cover and sprinkle with paprika and parsley.
Serves 4, but weigh out your 5 ounces.

CABBAGE ROLLS

1 large head cabbage
2 cans bean sprouts
14 oz. ground beef

2 C. tomato juice
1 onion, diced
Salt, pepper

Remove outer leaves of cabbage one by one; drop into boiling salted water and parboil for two minutes. NO LONGER!

Mix cut-up bean sprouts, beef, onion, salt, pepper and green pepper with mushroom pieces if desired. Place about one heaping tablespoon of mix on each leaf. The bigger the leaf, the more mix you use. Roll tightly. Place in a large kettle on top of all the leftover cabbage coarsely chopped. Pour on tomato juice and cook about 1-1/2 hours.

You'll need about 20 or more cabbage leaves depending on the size of the cabbage. Serves 2 for dinner. Keep an eye on the simmering cabbage rolls and if they begin to look dry, add more tomato juice or water. This is a very tasty and filling meal, and you can keep eating on your portion until you go to bed!

CASSEROLE SUPREME FOR TWO

14 oz. lean ground beef
2 cans French-style green beans, drained
1 can mushroom pieces, drained

1 large onion, sliced and separated into rings
2 ribs of celery in 1/2" pieces

Crumble hamburg in large casserole. Add other ingredients and mix well. Season to taste with salt, pepper, garlic salt, etc. Bake covered at 350° for 25 minutes. Remove cover and bake 10 minutes longer. Drain off all fat possible and serve hot. Equals 2 beef servings.

STUFFED FLOUNDER

14 oz. frozen fillets, thawed
1 can bean sprouts, drained
3 T. green onion tops
1/4 t. thyme

1/4 t. salt
Dash of ground pepper
1 C. Zippy Zero (see Dressings and Spreads)

Preheat oven to 350°. Mix chopped sprouts with seasoning. Spoon evenly over fillets and roll up, fastening with a toothpick. Place in a baking dish and pour Zippy Zero or tomato juice over the roll-ups. Bake about 30 minutes. Serves 2 for dinner.

SUPERB MEATLOAF

14 oz. ground beef
4 oz. carrots, grated
2 oz. celery, very fine dice
1 oz. green onions, very fine
    dice

1/2 green pepper, very fine
    dice
1/2 C. tomato juice
Salt, pepper, garlic powder
    as desired

If possible, put vegetables through blender or grinder. If
not, dice them very fine. The amount of vegetables will equal
equal about 1 cup. Combine with ground beef, tomato juice
and seasonings. Pack into pan (glass is best) and bake at
350° for about 1 hour and 10 minutes. Immediately pour off
all liquid. Cool meatloaf slightly before slicing. Serves
2 for dinner. This is the best meatloaf you've ever tasted.
You'll like it cold, too.

HADDOCK LEMONAISE

14 oz. fillet of haddock
1/4 lemon, seeded and cut up
1/2 clove garlic, optional
4 oz. stalk celery, cut up
1 t. Worcestershire sauce

1 t. oregano
1 t. parsley flakes
1 t. horseradish
Dash of Tabasco

Place all ingredients except fish in blender. Chop well.
Put fish on foil and spoon mixture over fillet. Close
tightly, bake at 325° about 30 minutes. Delicious on grill
too. Dinner for two.

SHISH KABOB

1-3/4 lbs. beef or lamb, cut
    into 1-1/2 inch cubes
1/2 C. vinegar
1 t. salt
1/4 t. pepper
1 bay leaf

Clove garlic, sliced
2 green peppers, cut in-
    to 1-inch pieces
1 large onion, cut into
    chunks
2 firm tomatoes, cut in-
    to 1-inch pieces--or
    use Cherry tomatoes

Marinate meat in mixture of vinegar, salt, pepper, and herbs
as desired in refrigerator for about 3 hours. Arrange mar-
inated meat and vegetables alternately on metal skewers.
Broil 3 inches from heat about 15 minutes or until tender.
Serves 4 for dinner with 1/2 fruit each. This is a real
summer must.

BOEUF EN GELEE

2 envelopes unflavored gelatin
1 C. cold water
2 beef bouillon cubes
1 T. horseradish
5 oz. cooked beef, cut into strips
1 can French style green beans, drained
1/4 C. red or green bell peppers, diced
2 green onions, minced

Sprinkle gelatin over 1 C. water in saucepan. Add bouillon cubes. Heat slowly and stir constantly until gelatin and bouillon cubes dissolve, about 5 minutes. Remove from heat, stir in horseradish and enough ice to bring to a total amount of 4 cups. Chill until thickened and fold in beef and vegetables. Chill until firm. Serves 1 for dinner.

CHICKEN BAR-B-QUE

1 C. Zippy Zero (see Dressings/ Spreads)
1 medium onion, chopped
1/4 t. each of ground cloves, cinnamon, allspice
1 t. dry mustard
1/4 t. garlic powder
1/4 t. hot crushed peppers
Sweetener if desired

Simmer sauce ingredients together until slightly thickened. Use on hot chicken in the broiler or outside on the grill, adding during the last half hour of cooking. This is so good you'll like it on beef, lamb, or veal. Dinner portion is 5 oz. cooked chicken.

GROUND BEEF CASSEROLE

7 oz. ground beef
4 small carrots, sliced
1/4 head shredded cabbage
2 stalks celery, sliced
1 small onion, diced
1 can bean sprouts, drained
1 C. tomato juice

Cook beef in heavy skillet and drain off all fat. Combine beef and other ingredients and bake in oven until carrots and cabbage are tender--about 1 hour at 350°. This recipe serves 1 for dinner. Use any spices or herbs that you wish. Bay leaf, garlic powder, etc.--whatever you do, this casserole is really great.

CAPE COD CASSEROLE

10 oz. cooked fish, (perch, cod, haddock) flaked
1 small can French style green beans, drained
1/2 head fresh cauliflower, broken into small pieces
1/2 C. skimmed milk
2 T. minced onions
1 t. imitation butter flavoring
Salt and pepper to taste
Pinch of nutmeg

Add onion flakes and butter flavoring to skimmed milk. Combine remaining ingredients in 2-quart casserole. Pour milk mixture over and bake covered, at 350° or until cauliflower is tender. Serves 2 for dinner, with 1/4 C. milk each. This basic casserole is a good base for many ingredients. Use your imagination and try many types of vegetables and spices. It's so good you can't possibly make a mistake.

CHICKEN TERIYAKI

1/2 C. soy sauce
1 t. ginger
1 t. dry mustard
2 T. brown sugar substitute
2 T. lemon juice
2 T. water
1 t. garlic salt
Pepper
1 broiler-fryer, skinned

Combine all but chicken in small saucepan and bring to a boil. Pour over chicken and marinate 2 hours or longer in refrigerator. A plastic bag is fine for marinating. You may grill the chicken outdoors or bake in the oven. Use the sauce to baste. Be sure to weigh your 5 ounces of chicken.

MEAT LOAF MAGIC

14 oz. ground beef
1/2 C. skimmed evaporated milk
1/4 C. tomato juice
Salt, pepper, garlic salt
1 T. Worcestershire sauce
1 T. salad mustard
1 large onion, or 1 T. dry onion flakes

Combine all ingredients, pack into a loaf pan. Bake at 325° for about 1 hour. Immediately pour off all liquid and fat. Cool meat loaf slightly before slicing. Serves 2 for dinner with 1/2 C. milk allowance for each.

CORDON BLEU VEAL

1-3/4 lb. veal, cut up
1 large tomato sliced (or 1 C. canned tomato
1 onion, minced
3 oz. can mushrooms, drained
4 oz. tomato juice
1 beef bouillon cube
1 C. boiling water
1 bay leaf

Brown meat slowly in Dutch oven. Stir in remaining ingredients. Season with salt and pepper. Simmer until tender—about 1 hour. You may add a bit more liquid if necessary. Serves 4 for dinner with 1/4 fruit each.

MEAT STUFFED ZUCCHINI

2 large zucchini
14 oz. hamburg
1 onion, chopped fine

1/2 C. Zippy Zero (see
Dressings and Spreads)

Cut squash lengthwise, remove seeds and sprinkle with salt
and pepper. Brown the hamburg in skillet with the onion.
Pour off all fat possible. Add Zippy Zero and mix well.
Fill squash and place in baking dish and bake for 45 minutes in 350° oven. Serves 2 for dinner.

CHICKEN FABRIZI

1 cut-up broiler-fryer, skinned
1 medium sized eggplant, peeled
and cut into strips
2 tomatoes, peeled and chopped

1 green pepper, cut into
strips
1 onion, chopped

Brown chicken under broiler. Remove to large casserole.
Add the other ingredients and pour on the following baste:

1/2 C. vinegar
1/2 C. water
3 T. lemon juice

1/2 t. salt
1/4 t. basil, thyme, or
both

Bake   covered in a 350° oven for 1 hour and then uncovered for 1/2 hour or until chicken is done. Entire
recipe equals 2 fruits, and be sure to weigh out your
5 ounces of chicken.

CREOLE FILLETS

1 lb. can tomatoes, pureed in
blender
1 C. chopped onions
1 C. chopped green pepper
1 clove garlic, minced

3 bay leaves
1-1/2 t. salt
Dash of cayenne
1-3/4 lbs. fish fillets

Cook onions, green pepper, garlic and bay leaves in
tomatoes. Simmer about 30 minutes until thickened.
Place fillets in baking dish. Cover with sauce and bake
about 30 minutes or until tender. Serves 4 for dinner
with 1 fruit and 5 oz. fish each.

BEEF SPROUTS STEW

14 oz. lean ground beef
3 stalks celery, chopped
2 medium-sized onions, chopped
1/4 green pepper, chopped
1-1/2 C. tomato juice

1 lb. can bean sprouts,
drained and rinsed
2 C. water
2 T. chili powder
1 T. Worcestershire sauce

Broil beef in patty form to medium done. Cut into small cubes. Set aside. Add celery, onions, and pepper pieces to water and cook for 10 minutes. Then add to this mixture tomato juice, beef, chili powder and bean sprouts. Cook very slowly for 1 hour. Add Worcestershire sauce just before serving. This serves 2 for dinner.

Do try this--it's really great.

POACHED FISH IN COURT BOUILLON WITH VELVET SAUCE

2 C. water
1 carrot, sliced
1 stalk celery
1 green onion, diced

1 lemon in slices
Spices as desired: bay
  leaf, tarragon, etc.
1 lb. fillet of sole

Combine water and vegetables and spices in a large skillet. Heat to boiling, then simmer for 10 minutes. Remove vegetables and spices. Add fish and simmer another 5 minutes, or until fish flakes easily. This is a true gourmet dish and so easy. 5 ounces of fish is your dinner portion.

Note: Overcooking the fish can make it tough and unappetizing. Don't let the liquid boil when cooking fish-- it will fall apart. Remove from liquid immediately when done or it will just keep on cooking even though you remove it from the burner.

VELVET SAUCE--Pour over fish as desired

10 oz. package frozen cauliflower
1 t. onion flakes
1 C. water

2-1/2 T. dry milk powder
1 t. yellow salad mustard
1 dill pickle, minced

Cook cauliflower and onion in water until soft. Puree in blender until smooth, return to saucepan. Add milk powder and stir briskly. Add mustard and pickle. Entire recipe equals 1/2 C. of milk. This sauce is very good over vegetables such as asparagus, too.

VEGETABLES

PERFECTION SALAD

2 envelopes unflavored gelatin
Sweetener to equal 1/2 C. sugar
1 t. salt
1 C. boiling water
1-1/2 C. ice water
1/2 C. vinegar
1 T. lemon juice (optional)

1-1/2 C. very finely
    shredded cabbage
1 C. very finely chopped
    celery
1/4 C. chopped pimiento
1/2 C. very finely chopped
    green pepper

Soften gelatin on 1/4 C. cold water. Add boiling water, sweetener, and salt. Stir well to dissolve. Stir in vinegar, lemon juice and ice water. When mixture begins to thicken, add the vegetables. Pour into a loaf pan or party mold or about 10 individual molds. This is very tasty and looks lovely for a buffet or luncheon. Try adding different raw vegetables such as radish pieces, small amounts of shredded carrots, very small cauliflowerettes, etc.

"POTATO" SALAD

2 packages or 1 head of cauli-
    flower, cooked (don't over
    cook)
2 dill pickles, chopped
1 cucumber, diced
1/2 green pepper, diced

2 big stalks celery,
    chopped fine
1/2 C. chopped green
    onions, green tops too
Enough Slim & Trim Mayon-
    naise to moisten

Like all potato salads--it's even better tomorrow. Top with paprika and pepper rings with pimiento pieces and it's gorgeous. Dress with Slim and Trim Mayonnaise (see Dressings and Spreads).

RED-FACED CAULIFLOWER

1 head cauliflower
2 C. tomato juice

1 T. salt
1/4 t. white pepper

Remove outer leaves and inside of core, leaving cauliflower whole. Place it stem up, in saucepan. Pour tomato juice and seasonings over it. Cover. Heat to boiling and simmer until cauliflower is just tender, about 20 minutes. Drain, place stem down in serving dish. Garnish with parsley if desired. Try a few dill seeds for a different flavor. This changes a bland vegetable into a very tasty dish.

CUCUMBER-ONION SALAD

2 large cucumbers
1 medium sized onion
4 T. buttermilk

2 T. white or wine vinegar
1 t. salt
1/4 t. pepper

Peel and thinly slice cucumbers and onion. Blend remaining ingredients and pour over vegetables. Marinate for several hours in the refrigerator. Just before serving sprinkle with parsley. Deduct buttermilk from milk allowance.

STEWED CELERY CREOLE

2 C. celery in 1" pieces
1 tomato, skinned and chopped
1 green pepper, minced
1 clove garlic, minced
Dry onion flakes
1 bay leaf

Basil, thyme, pepper, parsley to taste
1/4 t. chili powder
Dash of Tabasco
1 chicken bouillon cube
1/2 C. boiling water

Dissolve bouillon cube in boiling water. Add other ingredients and simmer, covered, until the celery is tender, about 20 minutes. Entire recipe equals one fruit.

CHINESE BEANS

2 packages frozen French
   style green beans
1 chicken bouillon cube
1 C. hot water

1 t. dry onion flakes
1/8 t. ginger
1/2 t. garlic salt
1 T. soy sauce

Simmer all but beans for 20 minutes. Toss beans in liquid and heat through. This is a tasty filler-upper!

BREADED TOMATOES

1 eggplant
1 fresh tomato cut into wedges
1 t. dry onion flakes
1 green pepper, sliced

1 t. horseradish
1/2 t. oregano
Dash of Tabasco

Peel, dice, and cook eggplant in boiling water for 5 minutes. Drain well. If in a hurry, blot with a paper towel. Combine remaining ingredients, pour over eggplant in casserole and bake uncovered at 350° for 45 minutes. This will make about 6 servings. The entire recipe equals one fruit.

GLAZED CARROTS

1 lb. carrots
1 C. unsweetened pineapple juice

2 chicken bouillon cubes
1/4 t. ground ginger

Slice carrots into thin discs. In a saucepan combine remaining ingredients and bring to a boil. Lower the heat, add carrot slices and simmer until the liquid is absorbed. Cook a few minutes more, shaking the pan constantly, until the slices are lightly glazed. Entire recipe is two fruit servings.

MARINATED MUSHROOMS

Lightly wash and drain fresh mushrooms. Put into boiling salt water. Squeeze juice of 1 lemon into boiling water to keep mushrooms white. Boil 3 minutes and drain. Cover mushrooms with white vinegar and add 3 crushed garlic cloves, 1 tablespoon basil and let stand 4 to 6 hours. Drain and serve for salads or eat as hors d'oeuvres on toothpicks.

PICKLED CARROTS

1 lb. carrots	1 t. salt
1 C. white vinegar	Sweetener to equal 1/4
1/4 C. chopped onion	C. sugar (if desired)
1 t. pickling spice	

Bring mixture of everything but carrots to a boil, reduce heat, then add quartered peeled carrots. Simmer for 5 minutes. Pour into shallow container, cool and chill for about 2 hours. Drain before serving. This is finger food so if you want your carrots less crisp, cut them thinner, or cook them longer.

RED AND GREEN SALAD

2 T. vinegar	Sweetener to taste
1 T. dry minced onion	1 lb. can French style
1/2 t. salt	green beans
Dash of pepper	1 C. diced radishes

Soften onion in vinegar for 5 minutes. Add to remaining ingredients. Let marinate in refrigerator for a couple of hours. Serve on lettuce leaves.

PICKLED BEANS

1/2 C. vinegar	1 lb. French style green
1 t. pickling spice	beans
	Sweetener, if desired

Simmer vinegar and pickling spice. Pour over beans that have been heated and drained. Marinate until cold or overnight. You may reheat to serve but they are good cold, too.

KRAUT SALAD

1 can sauerkraut, rinsed well
and cut with scissors
1/2 C. diced celery
1/2 C. green pepper, diced
1/4 C. carrots, shredded

1/2 C. vinegar
Dash of chives
Sweetener to equal 1/2 C.
sugar

Combine vinegar, sweetener and chives. Toss over combined
vegetables. Let stand--until tomorrow if you can. The
longer it marinates, the better it tastes.

SUBURBAN CABBAGE

2 lb. cabbage, shredded fine
1/4 C. hot water
1 chicken bouillon cube
1 small apple diced

1 onion, diced
1/4 t. caraway seeds
2 T. cider vinegar
1 T. Worcestershire sauce

Cook cabbage in water over low flame for 10 minutes. Add
the other ingredients and cook about 10 minutes more, until
cabbage is almost tender. Serve immediately. Entire recipe
is one fruit.

STEWED SUMMER SQUASH

1 # summer squash
1 C. Zippy Zero
1/2 T. dried green bell
peppers
1/2 T. dried onion flakes

1/4 t. celery seed
1/2 t. basil
1/2 t. oregano
Dash of garlic powder
Sweetener, if desired

Combine all but squash in a saucepan. Simmer about 5
minutes then add thinly sliced squash. Cook about 5-10
minutes more, or until squash is tender. A very colorful
dish to serve with fish.

BEAN SALAD

1 # can green beans,
drained
1 # can wax beans, drained
1 # can French-style green
beans, drained

1 C. sliced celery
1 medium green pepper,
in large dice or rings,
or strips
1 medium onion, thinly
sliced in rings, or diced

Dressing:
3/4 C. cider vinegar
Sweetener to equal 1/2 C. sugar
1/2 t. dry mustard
1/2 t. tarragon

1/2 t. basil (optional)
1/2 t. oregano
2 T. dry parsley flakes
or any amount fresh par-
sley desired

Mix all vegetables in a large bowl. Combine ingredients for dressing, drizzle over vegetables. Cover and marinate for several hours, or overnight. Stir them whenever you remember. May last for several meals, snacks, etc., and this dish really improves with age. You might try adding cooked carrots as another vegetable, too.

SWEET DILL SLICES

2 C. dill hamburg slices, rinsed and drained
1/2 C. cider vinegar
1/2 C. water

Sweetener to equal 1 C. sugar
1/4 t. celery seed
1/2 T. mustard seed
1/2 t. salt

Simmer all together about 3 minutes. Put chips in a pint jar, pour vinegar solution over them, cover tightly. By the time they're cool, they're sweet. Instead of the last three ingredients, try 1 T. pickling spice instead. You can save the sweet solution to use again. It's good for thinning LoMaize.

A PRETTY PICKLEMENT

2 envelopes gelatin
1/2 C. cold water
1 C. vinegar
Sweetener to equal 1/2 C. sugar

1 t. whole cloves
2 C. ice water
1 C. diced Sweet Dill Slices
4 oz. pimientos, rinsed, blotted dry, and diced

Sprinkle gelatin on 1/2 C. water to soften. Simmer together for 10 minutes the vinegar, sweetener, and cloves. Strain, add softened gelatin, place over low heat, and stir until gelatin is dissolved. Add ice water to equal 3 3/4 C. total volume, and chill to consistency of unbeaten egg white. Add pickles and pimientos, stirring to make sure they don't just float on top.

SLICED CUCUMBERS

2 cucumbers
1 T. salt
1/4 C. water

Salt, pepper
Sweetener if desired

Slice peeled cucumbers very thin. Sprinkle with salt and let stand half an hour. Drain. Mix remaining ingredients and pour over the cucumbers. Chill before serving.

54

DELICIOUS DUTCH COLE SLAW

1 C. buttermilk
1 1/2 t. lemon juice
1 1/2 t. liquid hot mustard
  or 1/2 t. dry mustard
Salt, pepper, nutmeg

1 1/2 t. artificial sweet-
  ner (or to taste)
1 head of cabbage
Several radish skins and/
  or 1 t. carrot shreds

Shred cabbage by hand or in blender. Combine other ingredients and mix well. Use only a mere pinch of nutmeg and
make sure it is thoroughly mixed. Chop radish skins very
fine and mix through the cabbage. Pour the liquid mixture over the cabbage. This recipe equals one glass of
milk. You may use skim milk instead of buttermilk, but
the dressing will be thinner.

RATATOUILLE

1 eggplant, peeled and diced
1/2 C. thinly sliced onions
2 summer squash, thinly
  sliced
1 green pepper, cut in long
  thin strips
3 tomatoes, thinly sliced

2 t. salt
1/2 t. ground pepper
1 clove garlic, minced
1 T. parsley
Pinch of marjoran, orega-
  gano, or basil

Cook eggplant and onion in boiling water for 10 minutes
and drain. Combine remaining ingredients with cooked
vegetables and layer in casserole. Bake at 350 degrees
about 30 minutes. Makes 6 servings of 1/2 serving fruit
(tomato) each. This may be served hot or cold.

DILLY BEANS

1 # fresh green beans
1 t. dry minced onion
1/2 C. chopped celery

1 clove garlic, minced
1 t. dillweed
1 t. dillseed

Cook beans and celery in small smount of boiling salt
water for about 10 minutes. Stir in remaining ingredients and simmer for another 10-15 minutes.

WILTED GREEN AND GOLD SALAD

10 oz raw spinach, washed,
  drained, cut bite-size
3 oranges, peeled and sliced
1 bunch green onions, dliced
1 bunch radishes, sliced

2 T. vinegar
2 T. orange juice
1/2 t. Tabasco
1/2 t. salt
1/4 t. dry mustard

Slices oranges over a bowl to catch the juice you'll
need for the dressing. Toss together the spinach, oran-
es, onions, and radishes. Mix together in small skillet

the vinegar, orange juice, Tabasco, salt, and mustard.
Heat and pour over the tossed salad. Serves 6 people,
1/2 fruit each.

PICKLED CAULIFLOWER

1 head of cauliflower   Liquid from a jar of dill
                                pickles

Pour liquid into a saucepan, add cauliflower broken into
flowerets and cook about 15 minutes, stirring to make
sure each piece gets its turn in the hot liquid. Cook
until tender-crisp, not mushy, and store in the refrigerator. Good to eat as a snack, too, and makes a lovely garnish for any main course.

IRISH POTATOES

Maybe the Irish only have this dish at Hallowe'en, but
we hobgoblins can have it anytime. It looks rather
complicated because you have three pans going at once,
but it goes together in a hurry the second time you make
it!

2 # cauliflower or 1 head   1 1/2 C. sliced green
3 t. salt   onions
4 C. coarsely shredded cabbage 1/3 C. skim milk
                                1/4 t. pepper

In pan 1, put 1/2" boiling water, 1 t. salt, and the
cauliflower. Cook it for 15-20 minutes, or until fork-
tender and completely cooked. Drain.

In pan 2, put 1/2" boiling water, 1/2 t. salt, and the
cabbage. Cook it 8-10 minutes until just tender. Drain.

In pan 3, heat green onions with milk and 1/2 t. salt.
Bring to a boil and then simmer for 10 minutes.

Now to assemble--beat cauliflower in blender with remaining 1 t. salt and 1/4 t. pepper. Beat in the onion and
hot milk combination, and beat in the cabbage mixture.
Heat for 5 minutes, in a double boiler if necessary.
Serve hot. Looks for all the world like mashed potatoes,
but tastes better! If it looks on the green side, that's
because you had new cabbage and lots of green onion tops.

APPLE RELISH

1 C. chopped cabbage   Sweetener to equal 1/3
1 chopped apple, with peel   C. sugar
1/4 C. chopped green pepper   1/2 t. salt
4 T. white vinegar   1/4 t. dry mustard
                                1/4 t. caraway seed

Mix vinegar, sweetener, and spices. Pour over combined cabbage, apple, and green pepper. This is a great way to eat your apple and have it too! The entire recipe equals ONE fruit.

DEVILISH BIG BOY

1 tomato, halved	1 t. minced green onion
1 t. prepared mustard	1/2 t. basil or dillweed
1 t. minced green pepper	

Place halves, cut side up in baking dish or pie pan. Spread with mustard, and sprinkle with peppers, onions, and herb. Bake in hot over (425 degrees) for 8 minutes. Although it's used as a vegetable, for purposes of the diet this is one fruit allowance.

SWEET-SOUR SLAW

3 C. finely shredded cabbage	1 T. vinegar
1 t. dry onion flakes	1/4 t. salt
1/2 t. celery salt	1/4 t. paprika
Sweetener to equal 1 T. sugar	1/2 C. Slim and Trim Sour Cream

To make Sour Cream: Combine 1/2 C. SKIMMED evaporated milk and 2 T. lemon juice and let stand at room temperature for 10 minutes. Now add the herbs and flavorings in the recipe, stir well, and pour over cabbage. Toss lightly. Entire recipe equals 1 C. of milk.

"DRESSING" FOR TURKEY

This will fool you, for it tastes for all the world like bread stuffing.

1 head cauliflower--cooked tender, but not mushy	
2 t. dry onion flakes	2 T. poultry seasoning
4 C. diced celery	Salt, pepper
1/2 C. minced green pepper	Canned mushrooms, if desired

Toss lightly and stuff bird. You may also bake in a separate dish and serve as you would your best holiday dressing. This recipe yields about 8 cups.

BERMUDA BEANS

2 cans green beans, drained   1 Bermuda onion, thinly
1 can mushroom bits, drained   sliced

Cover bottom of shallow baking dish with sliced onions.
Top with green beans and mushrooms, seasoned as desired
(garlic powder, soy sauce.) Cover with foil and bake at
350 degrees for 30 minutes or until onion is tender.
A few pimiento strips add a nice dash of color. Mix
onions through casserole before serving--and eat all you
want.

SUNNY SALAD

20 oz. can crushed pineapple   2/3 C. ice water
  unsweetened, drained   Sweetener to equal 1/4
2 packages or tablespoons   C. sugar
  gelatin   1/4 t. salt
1/2 C. cold water   2 T. vinegar
2/3 C. boiling water   1 C. grated carrots
Reserved juice from pineapple

Soften gelatin on cold water, dissolve in boiling water,
stirring well. Add sweetener, salt, vinegar, reserved
syrup and ice water. Chill. When mixture becomes thick,
add pineapple and carrots. Pour into 4 cup mold or individual serving dishes. Entire recipe equals 5 fruit
servings and really satisfies a craving for sweets.

GUSSIED-UP ASPARAGUS

2 packages gelatin   2 C. ice water
1/2 C. cold water   1 can asparagus,liquid
1 C. vinegar   reserved
1 t. whole cloves   Sweetener to equal 1/2
                                       C. sugar

Sprinkle gelatin on cold water to soften. Simmer vinegar
and cloves together for 10 minutes. Strain cloves from
vinegar, add softened gelatin to vinegar and place over
low heat until gelatin is dissolved. stirring constantly.
Remove from heat add ice water, sweetener, and liquid
from asparagus. There should be about 3 3/4 cups.
Chill to the consistency of an egg white and add asparagus. Pour into serving mold and chill until firm.
Your portion is whatever you desire.

TART PARTY CARROTS

2 C. finely diced carrots
1/2 C. diced celery
1/4 C. diced green pepper
2 green onions, minced

1 t. mustard seed
1/4 t. ginger
1/2 C. water
1/4 C. cider vinegar

Cook carrots in small amount of water for 10 minutes.
Drain and save 1/2 C. liquid. Mix carrots, celery,
green pepper, and onions. Combine the reserved liquid,
mustard seed, ginger, water, and vinegar and heat just
to boiling. Pour over vegetables and mix well. Chill
overnight. Eat as desired.

The uses for this are unlimited--side dish, on lettuce,
garnishes, or buffet fare.

SCRAMBLED CABBAGE

3 C. shredded cabbage
1 C. chopped celery
1 onion, diced fine
1 green pepper, chopped

1 t. salt
Dash of pepper
1 small tomato, cut into
  8 pieces

Place all ingredients except tomato in heavy skillet and
cook 10 minutes or until just tender. Now add tomato
pieces and finish cooking until just heated through.
Entire recipe equals 1 fruit serving.

PINEAPPLE CUCUMBER SALAD

2 packages unflavored gelatin
1 C. club soda or water
½ t. ginger
2 packets sweetener
20 oz. can unsweetened
  crushed pineapple

1 C. chopped celery
1/4 t. salt
1 large cucumber, grated
3 T. lemon juice
2 drops green food
  coloring

Drain and reserve juice from pineapple. In saucepan soften
gelatin on soda or water. Stir over low heat until dissolved.
Add ginger, sweetener, reserved pineapple juice, lemon juice,
salt, grated cucumber, food coloring and enough ice cubes to
make 4 cups total volume. Chill until thickened, then add
pineapple and celery and turn into loaf pan. Slice and serve
on lettuce. Recipe equals 5 fruit servings. Be sure to wash
the cucumber free of any wax or oil preservative.

WAX BEAN RELISH

1 # can wax beans, drained
1/4 t. salt
1 T. dry mustard
1/4 t. celery seed
Sweetener to equal 1/4 C. sugar, if desired

1/4 t. tumeric
1/2 C. wine vinegar
1/2 C. water or liquid
   from beans

Mix spices together in saucepan. Add liquids, bring to
a boil. Add beans and stir well. Remove from heat and
serve cold. You can also add your favorite ingredients
such as pimiento pieces or onion rings, etc. This is
a very good all around side dish for any occasion. Enjoy
it freely.

SWEET-SOUR CABBAGE

1 medium head of red
   cabbage
1/3 C. vinegar
1/3 C. water
4 oz. apple, grated and peeled

1/3 C. brown sugar subs-
   titute
1/2 t. caraway seeds
Dash of salt, pepper

Chop cabbage and place in saucepan. Add remaining ingredients and bring to a boil. Turn heat low and simmer
for about 1 hour. This is absolutely great. Very good
with Beef Sauerbraten. Entire recipe equals 1 fruit.

SPRING SALAD

2 packages unflavored gelatin
1/2 C. cold water
1 C. vinegar
1 t. whole cloves
Sweetener to equal 1/2 C. sugar
1/2 C. diced green pepper

3 C. ice water
1 C. finely shredded
   cabbage
1/2 C. minced celery
1/2 C. diced green onions

Sprinkle gelatin on cold water to soften. Simmer vinegar and cloves together about 10 minutes. Strain cloves
from vinegar, add softened gelatin and place over low
heat until gelatin is dissolved. Remove from heat and
add ice water and sweetener. There should be about 3 3/4
C. Chill to the consistency of egg whites. Then add
vegetables and pour into a plain or fancy mold. This is
a very good unlimited dish with a unique flavor.
Try it!

WALDORF SALAD

1 medium apple, chopped
1 small carrot, grated

1/2 C. chopped celery

Blend above ingredients with 1/4 C. LoMaize. Chill in refrigerator about 2 hours. Toss with desired amount of chopped lettuce. Entire recipe equals 1 fruit serving. This salad has a sweet nutty flavor.

NUTMEG CARROTS

1 # carrots, peeled, sliced
2 T. yellow salad mustard

2 T. brown sugar sub-
   stitute
1/4 t. nutmeg

Cook carrots in a small amount of boiling water about 15 minutes. Drain and then add other ingredients, stirring well to blend. The carrots have an unusual flavor and your whole family will enjoy them. Eat anytime.

GARDEN VEGETABLE MOLD

3 packages unflavored gelatin
4 1/2 C. water, divided
1/2 C. tarragon vinegar or
  dill pickle juice
Sweetener to equal 1/2 C. sugar
  (or less)

1 t. salt
1/4 C. green onion tops
1/2 C. chopped pimiento
1# can whole green beans,
  drained
4 oz. can mushroom bits,
  drained

Sprinkle gelatin over 1 C. of the water. Place over low heat, stir until gelatin is dissolved. Stir in remaining water, vinegar, sweetener, and salt. Chill until mixture mounds slightly, then add remaining ingredients. Turn into a large mold and chill until firm. This is a very pretty addition to the buffet table for lunch or summer supper.

YELLOW CAULIFLOWER

1 C. vinegar
1 C. water
Sweetener to equal 1/4 C. sugar
1/4 t. salt
1/4 t. celery seed

1/4 t. tumeric
1 T. dry mustard
1 large head of
  cauliflower

Combine liquids and spices. Bring to a boil. Add separated cauliflower and simmer about 15 minutes, stirring often so it all gets the pretty yellow color from the tumeric. Chill. This goes to picnics, makes great finger food and keeps in the refrigerator for anytime snacks.

DESSERTS
BAKED PEARS

Peel, core, and halve pears and place in shallow baking dish.
Sprinkle with cinnamon and nutmeg. Put 1 tablespoon water or
club soda in the bottom of the baking dish. Cover (aluminum
foil will do) and bake for about an hour until soft. Bake
very small pears whole. You can also spread a little food
coloring and water on the pears for color. One whole pear
equals one fruit.

PINEAPPLE ICE

1 C. buttermilk
1/2 C. crushed pineapple in
   pure juice
Dash of salt

1/2 t. vanilla, orange, or
   mint extract
Sweetener to equal 1/4 to
   1/2 C. sugar

Combine and freeze to mushiness or firmer if desired, using
individual molds or cartons. Cottage cheese cartons are
fine. If you put it in three paper drinking cups, you
can enjoy it three times during the day. This equals one
fruit and one cup of milk. Really good in popsicle molds
too.

FRUIT COBBLER

1 package gelatin
1/2 C. water
1 t. dry punch-flavor drink mix
3 packets sweetener
1¼ C. water

3 apples, peeled, cored,
and sliced into chunks
(or try fresh peaches,
plums, blueberries, or
strawberries)
1/2 C. skim milk powder

Place sliced fruit in baking dish. Soften gelatin on water,
heat to dissolve, add dry drink mix, sweetener, and rest of
water. Pour enough on fruit to just cover it. Now sprinkle
powdered skimmed milk evenly over the fruit. Bake at 350°
for 45 minutes, or until milk becomes crisp. Cool and refrigerate until jelled. This recipe counts as three fruits
and 12 oz. liquid skim milk.

MAPLE MOUSSE

1 package unflavored gelatin
2 C. water
2 t. instant coffee

1 capful maple flavoring
1 t. nonfat dry milk
   powder
Sweetener as desired

Soften gelatin in 1/2 cup cold water. Bring 1-1/2 cups water
to boil. Add coffee, sugar substitute, maple flavor, and
gelatin mixture. Mix well and chill. When jelled, put
through blender with dry milk for 10-15 seconds. Refrigerate.
This mixture will jell in about 1/2 hour in the refrigerator
after blending. This is unlimited. However, if several portions are consumed, deduct powdered milk from daily allowance.

LIME SHERBET

1 package unflavored gelatin   1 package lime flavored drink
1/2 C. cold water   mix, unsweetened
1/2 C. boiling water   Sweetener to equal 2 C.
1 quart skim milk   sugar

Soften gelatin in cold water; dissolve in boiling water.
Add drink powder, sweetener and milk. Pour into freezing
tray and freeze until solid 1" from edges. Stir with fork
and refreeze. If you freeze this recipe in ice cube trays
and then put the cubes in plastic bags, they are handy for
Greenland Coolers (see Drinks). One fourth of the entire
recipe is one milk serving.

CUSTARD

2 C. skim milk   1 rennet tablet
Sweetener to equal 3 T. sugar   1 T. cold water
1 t. vanilla

Set out 4 dessert cups. Combine milk, sweetener, and
flavoring. Heat to lukewarm only. (Test on inside of
wrist!) Soften rennet tablet in cold water. Add to warm
milk and stir for a few seconds, then pour at once into
dessert cups. Let stand undisturbed for 10 minutes, then
chill. Try this with various flavoring and food colors.
Entire recipe equals 2 glasses of milk.

Almond Cream	1/2 t. almond extract, 2 drops yellow color
Lemon Cream	1/2 t. lemon extract, 4 drops yellow
Orange Cream	1 t. orange extract, 3 drops yellow
Peppermint Cream	1/8 t. extract, 2 drops red

PICKLED PEARS

4 firm, slightly under-ripe pears   1 T. whole cloves
1/2 C. white vinegar   1 stick cinnamon
1/2 C. water   Few drops green food
Sweetener to equal 1 C. sugar   coloring

Quarter, core, and peel pears. Combine all ingredients but pears and bring to a boil. Simmer 5 minutes. Add pears, simmer until tender, about 20 minutes. This equals 4 fruits. Try peaches instead of pears, but simmer them only 10 minutes.

GINGER MELON MOLD

2 envelopes unflavored gelatin   2½ C. ice water
½ C. cold water   Honeydew melon cubes cut
1 C. boiling water   from a 2" wedge, sprink-
½ t. ginger   led with ginger
6 packets sweetener

Soften gelatin on cold water and add boiling water. Stir to dissolve. Add ginger, sweetener, and ice water. Chill until thick, add melon cubes and pour into 1 quart mold.

When serving, use mint garnish and a mere dusting of finely ground ginger. This entire recipe equals one fruit.

CRANBERRY FLUFF

2 envelopes unflavored   2 C. cranberries and 3/4
   gelatin softened in 1/4 C.   C. water simmered
   cold water   until they pop

Add gelatin mix to cranberry mix and add 1 package orange Kool-Aid and sweetener to equal 1 C. sugar.

Add ice water to bring mixture up to 3 cups. Let set until thickened.

In chilled bowl, beat: 1/3 C. dry milk
                           1/3 C. ice water
                           2 T. lemon juice

When it's like whipped cream, fold into cranberry mix. Pour into your prettiest glasses and serve with a sprig of mint. One fourth of entire recipe equals 1 fruit and 1/4 cup milk.

GINGERED APPLESAUCE

2 C. unsweetened applesauce   1 t. grated orange rind
1 t. ginger   Sweetener to equal 1 C.
                            sugar

Mix all together in saucepan and heat slowly. Simmer for 10 minutes. Serve hot or cold. Equals FOUR fruit servings. Note: Orange rind grates better if it's frozen first.

APPLE CREAM MOUSSE

1 C. unsweetened apple sauce
1 package unflavored gelatin
1/2 C. water

Sweetener to equal 1 C. sugar
4 oz. skimmed evaporated milk
frozen almost solid in
bowl

Soften gelatin in 1/2 C. cold water. Heat applesauce, add sweetener and flavor with cinnamon and nutmeg. Add gelatin and stir to dissolve. Beat milk until it's like whipped cream, fold in applesauce mix very gently and chill until firm. Serve within four hours. Serves 2, the equivalent of 1 fruit and 1/2 cup milk.

FLUFF

1/3 C. dry powdered milk
1/3 to 1/2 C. ice water

1-1/2 T. lemon juice
Sweetener to equal 1/4 C.
sugar

With a spoon, mix the milk and water in your mixing bowl. Now place in freezer for about 1/2 hour, until thoroughly chilled. Beat in electric mixer until frothy. Add lemon juice and sweetener. Beat until it's stiff like whipped cream. This huge bowlful equals 1 cup of milk and tastes out of this world.

Fluff is the basis for many sudden desserts. Here are suggestions:

Pineapple Fluff: Add 1/2 C. unsweetened crushed pineapple. (Add juice to mix as it's whipping, and fold in pineapple by hand when it's stiff.)

Welsh Apple Fool: Grate in the blender one or two apples, and fold into whipped mix with cinnamon and nutmeg. (Don't forget to count fruit allowance.)

Orange Fluff: Put a peeled, quartered orange through blender. Add juice to mix as it's whipping and fold in orange by hand. The orange juice seems to "cook" the fluff. Try this, it's entirely different from the others. (Don't forget to deduct fruit from fruit allowance.)

Berry Fluff: 1/2 C. strawberries, raspberries, etc.-- just delightful.

And if you've already used up your fruit allowance for the
day, look for an extract to flavor this--banana extract,
almond extract, coconut extract, mint and pink coloring.
This recipe has endless variations.

BAKED APPLE

Core 9 apples. Place close together in 8" square pan and
pour 8 oz. of our red punch pop over them. Sprinkle cinnamon
and a dash of nutmeg over them and bake until soft. If desired, serve with a spoonful of Fluff on top. Flavor the
batch of Fluff with cinnamon and nutmeg, too. The apples are
just as good cold as they are hot, too.

CRANBERRY DESSERT

2 packages unflavored gelatin
1 package strawberry flavored
   drink mix, unsweetened

20 oz. can unsweetened
   crushed pineapple,
   drained
2 C. cranberries, frozen
   and ground in the
   blender

Soften unflavored gelatin on 1/2 C. cold water. Add 1 C.
boiling water and dry strawberry powder. Add 2 C. ice
water (should include the juice from the pineapple),
sweetener to equal 1 C. sugar. Chill until syrupy, and
fold in cranberries and pineapple. This entire recipe
equals nine servings of fruit.

BLANC CREME

1 package unflavored gelatin
2 C. liquid skimmed milk
Sweetener to equal 1/2 C. sugar

1/4 t. salt
1/2 t. vanilla

Stir gelatin into 1/2 cup milk to soften. Add sweetener.
Place over low heat until gelatin is completely dissolved.
Remove from heat, add 1-1/2 cups milk, salt, and vanilla.
Stir well before pouring into mold. Chill until firm.

This basic recipe is a good base for experimentation. Try
substituting orange, lemon, peppermint, or rum extract for
vanilla. Also powdered instant coffee has a marvelous
effect on this creme. When using instant coffee, be sure
to dissolve it well in a small amount of liquid before
adding to the mixture.

KEY LIME FLUMMERY

1 package unflavored gelatin	1/2 C. lime juice
2 T. cold water	1/2 C. ice water
1/2 C. boiling water	3 drops green food coloring
Sweetener to equal 1 C. sugar	8 oz. <u>skimmed</u> evaporated milk

Chill milk in large mixing bowl, with beater, until ice crystals form around the edges, about 1" wide.

In the meantime, soften gelatin on cold water, dissolve in boiling water, stirring well, and add sweetener, lime juice, ice water and coloring. Chill until syrupy.

Beat milk until it is stiff like whipped cream, then add the gelatin mixture, beating well to combine. Spoon into 8 parfait glasses. This has a delightful tart flavor. Entire recipe equals 2 cups of milk.

LEMON BISQUE

Substitute lemon juice for lime juice, using yellow food coloring. Add 2 C. crushed unsweetened pineapple, using its juice in the gelatin mixture. Pour into two aluminum foil pie pans if you like, and freeze. Yummy! Entire recipe equals 2 cups of milk and four fruit servings.

LAYERED PINEAPPLE SLICES

20 oz. can pineapple slices in pure juice	1 recipe ANY FLAVOR GELATIN made in Lime flavor (see SNACKS & SOUPS)

Make lime gelatin, using juice from pineapple can to soften gelatin on, instead of water. When gelatin is nearly set, put a layer in bottom of empty pineapple can, add one pineapple ring, put in freezer until set, about 2 minutes, add another layer of gelatin and pineapple ring, let set, and repeat until you have used 5 slices in the can. If you don't have a second can handy for the rest of the slices, use sauce dishes for individual servings. Entire recipe counts as FIVE fruit servings. To unmold at serving time, run a thin knife blade around the inside of the can to loosen gelatin from can. Set the can in warm water for 5 seconds, turn upside down on tray. Slice into 5 separate rings, having gelatin on each side of the pineapple ring.

PINEAPPLE WHIP

1 package unflavored gelatin	1/8 t. salt
Sweetener to equal 1/3 C. sugar	2 C. unsweetened pineapple juice

Mix gelatin, sweetener and salt in a small saucepan. Add 1/2 cup of the pineapple juice. Place over low heat, stirring constantly until gelatin is dissolved. Remove from heat and stir in remaining 1-1/2 cups of pineapple juice. Chill until slightly thicker than unbeaten egg white consistency. Beat with a rotary beater, or electric beater until light and fluffy and double in volume. Spoon into 4 dessert dishes and chill until firm. Serves 4, with each serving equal to 1/2 C. fruit juice.

SKYROCKET

6 oz. evaporated skimmed milk
Sweetener to equal 1/2 C. sugar
3 oz. (1/2 can) frozen unsweetened
  orange juice, thawed

2 drops red food coloring
3 drops yellow food coloring

Put milk in mixing bowl and chill, with beaters, in freezer until ice crystals form at least 1" wide around the bowl. Then beat until it is stiff. Add remaining ingredients, mixing well. Pour into 5 cup mold, cover tightly with aluminum foil, and freeze. Entire recipe is equal to 1-1/2 cups milk and 1-1/2 cups orange juice. This easily-made dessert tastes like orange sherbet.

FRUIT COMPOTE

1 apple, diced
1 orange, sliced
1 peach, sliced
2 plums, sliced

2 apricots, sliced
1/2 C. crushed pineapple
  in pure juice

All fruits should be medium sized. To skin peach or apricots, dip into boiling water for 30 seconds, then plunge into cold water to stop the cooking process. Skins will then slip off.

To prepare this compote, work over a bowl to catch any juices, combine prepared fruits. Chill. Makes 6 servings. You may add a drop of sweetener to the compote, if desired, as well as 1/2 t. brandy or coconut extract.

ORANGE CANTALOUPE

2 packages unflavored gelatin
1 package orange flavored
  unsweetened drink mix
Dash of salt
Sweetener to equal 1 C. sugar

1/2 t. ginger
1/2 medium size canta-
  loupe, cut in pieces
  or balls

In a 4-cup measure put 1/2 cup of cold water and sprinkle
the gelatin on it. Add 1-1/2 cups of boiling water and stir
to dissolve. Add Kool-Aid, sweetener, salt, and ginger.
Fill with ice cubes and when about jelled, add cantaloupe.
Equals 1 fruit.

SUNSHINE SHERBET

2 T. unflavored gelatin
1/2 C. cold water
1-1/2 C. hot water
Sweetener to equal 2 C. sugar

1/2 C. lemon juice
4 C. unsweetened orange juice
3 C. water
32 oz. (4 C.) "Our
    Gingerale"

Soften gelatin on cold water and dissolve in hot water. Cool.
Cool. Add sweetener to taste, lemon juice, orange juice,
water and gingerale. Freeze in your ice cream freezer.
Remove dasher and pack and let stand for 3 or 4 hours.
Makes 1 gallon delicious sherbet. Entire recipe equals 8
servings of fruit.

PEACHES AND CREAM

2 sliced peaches, crushed
1 T. lemon juice
Sweetener to equal 2 T. sugar

1 T. gelatin
2 T. cold water
1 recipe of FLUFF

Stir together peaches, lemon juice, sweetener and salt. In
small saucepan soften gelatin in cold water, then place
over low heat to dissolve gelatin. Stir in peach mixture.
Chill. When almost set, whip up the FLUFF and mix in the
peaches, folding gently. Put into 4 dessert or parfait
glasses and freeze, covering tops with foil or plastic
wrap. Before serving, let stand at room temperature for
30 minutes. Entire recipe, including FLUFF, equals 1 milk
and 2 fruits.

CRANBERRY SHERBET

1 C. water
2 C. fresh cranberries
Sweetener to equal 3/4 C. sugar
1/4 C. cold water

1 package unflavored gela-
    tin
1/2 lemon, seeded and
    peeled
1 orange, seeded & peeled

Put water, cranberries into saucepan and simmer until the
skins pop. Soften gelatin on cold water and then stir into
cranberries. Add sweetener. Put this mixture into an
electric blender, add lemon and orange pieces, cover and
blend until liquefied and smooth. Pour into freezer tray
and freeze until mushy. Return to blender, cover and whip
until fluffy. Pour into 1 quart container, cover and freeze
until firm. Entire recipe equals 5 fruit servings.

PINEAPPLE MOUSSE

1 lb. can crushed pineapple in pure juice, drained and chilled
2 envelopes unflavored gelatin
1/3 C. cold water
3/4 C. boiling water
1 C. juice from pineapple (add water if necessary)
1/4 t. salt
Sweetener to equal 3/4 C. sugar
1 recipe FLUFF (without sweetener)

Soften gelatin on cold water. Add boiling water and stir to dissolve. Add juice, salt and sweetener. Place in re- frigerator until thick. Make the FLUFF and beat in the gelatin mix and fold in the chilled, crushed pineapple. Turn into a 6 cup mold and chill until serving time. En- tire recipe equals 4 fruits and 2 cups of milk.

MOCHA PUDDING

1 package unflavored gelatin
½ C. cold coffee
½ T. chocolate extract
2 C. skim milk
2 packets sweetener
¼ t. vanilla

Soften gelatin on coffee. Over low heat, stir to dissolve. Add extract, milk, sweetener and vanilla. Chill until thick. This is not a molded pudding. Entire recipe is two glasses of milk. If you desire a molded pudding, reduce total milk to 1½ cups.

PINEAPPLE CHIFFON PARFAIT

1-1/2 C. unsweetened pineapple juice
2 T. lemon juice
1/4 t. salt
2 envelopes unflavored gelatin
1/3 C. cold water
4 drops yellow food color- ing
Sweetener to equal 1/2 C. sugar
1 C. skimmed evaporated milk

Combine juices and salt. Bring to a boil. Soften gelatin on water and add to hot juice, stirring to dissolve. Add food coloring and sweetener. Chill until thick and syrupy. Place milk in a mixing bowl with the beaters, and chill in the freezer until ice crystals form 1" wide around the edges. Beat until stiff. Add syrupy mix 1/3 at a time and beat well. Add a dash of nutmeg and pour into serving glasses. Entire recipe equals 3 fruits and 2 glasses of milk.

Peach Parfait--made as above using 1 lb. can water-pack peaches instead of pineapple juice.

PEACHY MOLD

1 envelope unflavored gelatin
1/4 C. cold water
1 C. buttermilk
1 T. lemon juice

Sweetener to equal 1/4 C.
  sugar
1/2 t. almond extract
Yellow food coloring
3 peaches, cut up

Sprinkle gelatin on cold water in saucepan. Place over
low heat and stir until gelatin dissolves, about 3 to 5
minutes. Remove from heat, add buttermilk, lemon juice,
sweetener, flavoring and food color (a few drops will do).
Chill until mixture is the consistency of egg whites.
Layer the mixture and peaches in 3 tall glasses. Chill
until firm. Entire recipe may also be molded in a loaf
pan or a 2 cup mold and then sliced and served on lettuce
leaves. This recipe equals 3 fruits and 1 milk.

BLUEBERRY FROSTIE

1/2 C. frozen unsweetened blueberries

1/2 C. buttermilk
Sweetener to taste

Mix together and let set for about 5 minutes. Then start
stirring it together. The blueberries will freeze the
buttermilk and you'll soon have a luscious blueberry confection. May be frozen in freezer too. Entire recipe
equals 1 fruit and 1/2 C. milk.

PINEAPPLE BISQUE

2 envelopes unflavored gelatin
Sweetener to equal 1/2 C.
  sugar
2 T. lemon juice
3 drops yellow food coloring

20 oz. can unsweetened
  pineapple drained,
  juice reserved
10 oz. skimmed evapora-
  ted milk

Chill milk in a large mixing bowl with beaters, until ice
crystals form around the edges about 1"wide.

In small saucepan soften gelatin on 1/2 C. reserved pineapple juice. Dissolve over low heat, stirring constantly.
Remove from heat, add sweetener, lemon juice, food coloring and remaining juice. Chill until thick as egg white.

Beat chilled milk until stiff like whipped cream and
then add gelatin mix, beating well to combine. Fold in
crushed pineapple. Pour into parfait glasses or two foil
pie pans. One fifth (1/5) of recipe equals 1/2 C. milk
and 1 fruit serving. This dessert may be refrigerated
until serving time the same day, or covered and frozen
for a make-ahead dessert.

ITALIAN FRUIT COMPOTE

1 pint strawberries	1 small pineapple
1 apple	1½ C. our red pop
1 orange	

Cut fruit into small pieces and mix the fruits together.
Pour our red pop over the fruit and let set about 10 minutes. Then it is ready to eat. Will keep for 2 or 3 days in
the refrigerator. Entire recipe is 8 fruits.

ICE CREAM

Make custard with rennet tablet, but pour into a freezer
tray. Let stand undisburbed for 10 minutes, then place
in freezer until firm. Remove to bowl, break up with
fork and beat until smooth, but still a thick mush.
Finish freezing.

SNACKS & SOUPS

GASPACHO

This is the classic Spanish cold soup. It's wonderful in hot weather and should be served with a couple of ice cubes in each soup dish.

2 medium size tomatoes, cut into tiny bits
1 green onion, minced
1 small cucumber, unpeeled and minced
2 canned pimientoes, minced
1 or 1/2 green pepper, minced
2 stalks celery, minced

2 t. herb vinegar (tarragon, basil, or thyme)
1 clove garlic, minced
1 C. ice water
Dash of Tabasco
Liberal helping of coarsely ground black pepper
Dash of soy sauce

For best results mince all vegetables extremely fine and let soup season in refrigerator for several hours. This equals 2 fruit servings.

"CRISP"ROOMS

Canned button mushrooms, drained   Coarse salt

Spread mushrooms on cookie sheet. Sprinkle generously with coarse salt. Bake at 250° for about 1 hour or until mushrooms are completely dry. Turn at least once so they dry evenly. These are crisp and delicious and make you think you are eating popcorn, peanuts, or potato chips!

TV "FARE"

Watch TV and nibble to your hearts content--and lose weight besides!

Radishes   Garlic Powder   Soy Sauce

Clean radishes and make several cuts or gores at the widest part. Pour soy sauce into a deep bowl and put radishes in to soak for about 5 minutes. Remove and place radishes on a tray or plate and sprinkle with garlic powder--as much or as little as you wish.

This is also great on raw cauliflower bits.

Try this as an appetizer with your next dinner party and don't be surprised if non-dieters just rave about them too!

SWEET AND SOUR SOUP

5 c. beef bouillon
1 small cabbage, shredded
1 lb. can tomatoes
1 t. salt
1/8 t. pepper

Juice of 1/2 lemon
Sweetener to equal 1 T.
  sugar
1 t. dry minced onion

Simmer together for 1-1/2 hours. This recipe equals 4 fruit servings. If you don't want to part with fruit allowance, substitute 2 cups of tomato juice or 2 cups Zippy Zero for the tomatoes. Delicious!

CHICKEN "NOODLE" SOUP

2 C. chicken broth defatted, or
  2 C. chicken bouillon
1 can bean sprouts, drained
  and washed

1/2 t. dry onion flakes
1/2 t. red bell pepper
  flakes
1/2 t. celery salt

Simmer drained, washed bean sprouts and spices together in broth for 20 minutes, or more. Without any chicken in it, it's unlimited, so help yourself!

PICCALILLI

1 C. chopped celery
1 C. chopped green or red peppers
½ C. sliced green onions

1 C. Sweet Dill Pickles
  (P. 54)
2 oz. jar pimento pieces

Cook first three ingredients in juice from pickles. Add pickles and pimentos, chop fine and chill. Serve atop hamburgs if desired.

MING SOUP

2 chicken bouillon cubes
2 C. boiling water
1 can bean sprouts, drained
1 can French-style green beans
1 small can sliced mushrooms

1 C. cabbage, shredded
1 leaf Chinese cabbage,
  cut up
1/2 t. dry mustard
1/2 t. poultry seasoning,
  sage, or thyme

Bring bouillon cubes and water to boil and lower heat. Add drained vegetables and let simmer for 10-15 minutes. Dissolve mustard and seasoning in 1/4 C. water and add to soup just before serving.

VEGETABLE MARINADE

This marinade is wonderful for cucumber slices, carrot sticks, radishes, and cauliflower pieces. Marinate not much longer than 6 hours. It can be as little as 2 hours. Use thick slices of cucumber and small carrot sticks. Be sure to cover the vegetables and marinade.

3 parts vinegar
1/2 part water
Dry onion flakes
1/2 to 1 t. oregano and chives

Sprinkle of garlic powder
and parsley
Salt and pepper to taste

ANY FLAVOR GELATIN

2 packages unflavored gelatin
1 package drink mix, unsweetened

1/4 t. salt
Sweetener to equal 1 C.
sugar

In a 4-cup measure, or quart jar, put 1/2 cup of cold water and sprinkle on it 2 packages unflavored gelatin. Add 1-1/2 cups of boiling water and stir well to dissolve gelatin. Add flavored powder of your choice, salt, sweetener, and fill jar with ice cubes or water and stir well. Pour into serving dish to jell. Good anytime, any flavor.

RHUBARB UNLIMITED

4 C. diced rhubarb
3 C. water
Sweetener to equal 1 C. sugar
2 envelopes unflavored gelatin

1/2 C. cold water
1 t. strawberry flavored
drink mix, unsweetened

Cook rhubarb and the water together for about 5 minutes. Add sweetener and gelatin which has been softened in 1/2 cup cold water. Add strawberry flavored powder and chill until set. If you want more strawberry flavor than rhubarb, use the whole package of drink powder!

ROOM MATES

4 oz. can mushrooms, undrained
1 t. dry onion flakes

1 T. soy sauce
1 can bean sprouts, drained

Simmer mushrooms, onion flakes, and soy sauce together for 15 minutes. Add the sprouts and heat thoroughly. Good hot or cold, so keep them handy.

NOTHINGNESS

1 can French-style green beans

1/4 C. Ketchip (see Dressings & Spreads)

Drain and chill the green beans and moisten with Ketchip.
And don't offer any to non-dieters unless you have plenty
of beans and Ketchip on hand!

CURRY MOLD

1 envelope unflavored gelatin   1 t. curry powder
2 C. hot chicken bouillon

Soften gelatin on 1/4 cup of cold water, dissolve in bouillon
and add curry powder. Pour into ring mold which has been
rinsed with cold water. Unmold on lettuce covered plate,
and serve with cucumber slices, dill pickle rounds, radish
discs, celery, etc. Makes a great do-it-ahead appetizer.

"POTATO" SOUP

4 oz. raw cauliflower, chopped   1/2 t. dry onion flakes
2 oz. celery, minced   1/3 C. skim milk

Simmer the cauliflower, celery, and onion flakes with one
cup of water, or a little more if needed, until soft. Put
through blender to puree, return to heat, add salt, pepper,
and skim milk. Makes a great cup of potato soup. Don't
forget to deduct milk from your daily allowance.

TOMATO SOUP

Heat 6 ounces of tomato juice and dissolve one beef or
chicken bouillon cube in it. Add dry onion flakes or
garlic powder, salt, and pepper to taste. If desired,
add sliced mushrooms or minced green peppers.

FRESH ONION SOUP

3 cups chicken bouillon   1 T. soy sauce
3/4 cup sliced green onions,   1 t. imitation butter flavor
   tops and all   (optional)

Simmer bouillon and onions together for several minutes or
until tender--don't cook out the crunch. Add soy sauce and
liquid butter flavor.

CREAM OF ASPARAGUS SOUP

1 package frozen cauliflower   1 C. skim milk
1 lb. can asparagus   1 t. onion salt

Cook cauliflower in small amount of water for 5 minutes.
Into large blender container put asparagus, liquid and
solids, the cauliflower, milk, and onion salt. Blend well.
Heat in saucepan without boiling. Entire recipe equals 1
cup of milk.

CURRIED TOMATO JUICE

1 quart of tomato juice   Juice from 2 lemons
2 t. curry powder

Combine all ingredients; heat to boiling. Good hot as a
soup or cold as a pick-me-up drink.

BREAD AND BUTTER PICKLES

1 quart sliced cucumbers soaked in salt water 3 or 4 hours

To 1 quart pickles, add:

1 C. water   1 t. celery seed
1 C. vinegar   1 t. mustard seed
1 t. ground mustard   1 t. salt
Sweetener to equal 1 C. sugar   1/2 t. tumeric
1 onion, sliced   1/2 t. alum

Let come to a boil, pour into 3 sterilized pint jars. If
you use the two piece lids, when they are cool they go
"ping" and you know that they are sealed properly. They
may also be stored in the refrigerator without sealing.

CAVIAR

You might like to color this red.

1 eggplant   1/4 C. water
4 green onions, minced fine   1 T. lemon juice
1/4 C. Ketchip (see Dressings   Salt, pepper, garlic powder
   & Spreads)   Another 1/4 C. Ketchip

Wash eggplant and wrap in aluminum foil. Bake in 450° oven
about 45 minutes or until tender. Peel and chop fine.

In saucepan combine onions, Ketchip and water. When onions
are tender, add eggplant, lemon juice, salt, pepper, and
garlic powder. Add another 1/4 C. Ketchip, mix well and
chill. This keeps well several days in the refrigerator
and makes a spicy dip for cucumbers, celery, etc.

BLACK WALNUT CANDY

Some people over the years have become convinced that they
don't like milk. Here's the equivalence of two cups in
disguise.

2/3 C. dry milk powder
3 T. hot coffee
1/2 t. black walnut
   flavoring

1 t. sesame seeds
Sweetener for 1 T. sugar
   (optional)

Toast sesame seeds until golden. In an 8" aluminum foil pie plate mix the powdered milk and sweetener. Mix together the hot coffee and black walnut flavoring. Add to the milk and stir well. Mix in the sesame seeds and place in freezer. You can use the pan you mixed it together in, if you like. Break off a bite of this frozen confection whenever your sweet tooth has a craving ache. This is one way to get your milk!

NOW EAT YOUR MILK

Some people swear by this method of consuming milk and others swear at it! (And some won't give up their Fluff and Slim and Trim Malted to try milk in any other manner!)

1 apple grated
Few drops of vanilla
Dash of sweetener

1/4 t. nutmeg
2/3 C. dry milk powder

Mash all ingredients together, drop by 1/2 teaspoon onto teflon pan. Bake 20-25 minutes at 350 degrees. If you don't have a teflon pan, use aluminum foil on a regular cookie sheet. Four cookies equal 1/2 cup milk and 1/4 fruit. This recipe makes 16 cookies.

CREAM OF TOMATO SOUP

1/2 C. tomato juice
1/2 C. skim milk

Slice of onion
Dash of cloves

Heat tomato juice and onion slice. In a separate pan, heat milk. Combine the two hot mixtures stirring constantly, and add a dash of cloves, salt, and pepper. This will chase away the cold weather blues in a hurry. This recipe equals 1/2 C. milk.

VEGETABLE QUICK DIP

3 T. yellow salad mustard
Sweetener as desired

1 T. brown mustard

Mix mustards and sweetener in small dish. Use this as a really different quick dip for sliced radishes, raw cauliflower, green pepper strips, celery and carrot strips. It's also good mixed sparingly in a green salad. (You might want to thin it with juice from dill pickles for a salad dressing.)

CABBAGE SOUP

(A great ammunition in the battle of the overweight.)

4 C. chicken bouillon
1/2 head of cabbage, shredded
1 t. dry minced onion

1 T. lemon juice
Dash of sweetener, if
    desired

Simmer all ingredients for an hour or more. This is
marvelous with dinner, but try having it simmering on
the stove if you think you might be in danger of having
an acute attack of appetite.

CARROT SPREAD

1 # carrots, cut up
2 T. dried pepper flakes
2 T. hot water
2 T. yellow salad mustard

2 green onions, tops
    and all
1/2 C. LoMaize, room
    temperature

Soften pepper in hot water and comgine with carrots,
onions, LoMaize and mustard in blender. Chop until all
are blended together. This spread will keep for more
than two weeks in the refrigerator and makes the prettiest stuffed celery sticks imaginable. Use it in the
evening too as a dip with cauliflower, radishes, pepper
strips, etc.

BISTRO SOUP

2 to 4 beef bouillon cubes
4 C. water
1/2 head cabbage, shredded

1 # can wax beans
4 oz. can mushroom bits
    and pieces

Dissolve cubes in water, bring to a gentle boil. Add
cabbage, wax beans, and mushrooms, including the juice
they are packed in. You may flavor as desired with
pepper, onion, etc, If you add 1/2 t. chili powder the
flavor is very unusual. Not only is this soup delicious,
but it's an anytime snack.

SUMMER SOUP

1 # can pimientos
2 C. tomato juice

3 C. chicken bouillon

Drain pimientos, rinse with cold water and put through
a sieve or blender. Add tomato juice and chicken bouillon and simmer for 5 minutes. Stir in 1 t. lemon juice
and add salt and pepper to taste. Chill the soup
thoroughly before serving. This is very tasty and
different, and an anytime snack.

VEGETABLE SOUP

2 C. water
2 beef bouillon cubes
3 C. tomato juice
½ head cabbage, chopped
1 C. chopped celery
Bunch of green onions, chopped
1 C. diced carrots
1 T. parsley flakes
salt, pepper
Desired herbs for flavor

Put all together in a large kettle and simmer for 2 or more hours to develop flavor. Good anytime.

RATATOUILLE

1 small eggplant
2 zucchini squash
1 bunch green onions
1 green pepper
2 small tomatoes (½#)
3 cloves garlic
1 t. basil

Pare and cube eggplant, zucchini, add chopped onions, pepper, tomatoes, and seasoning. Cook over low heat, uncovered, until thick, about 30 minutes or more. Good hot or cold. Entire recipe is 2 fruits.

CUCUMBER SOUP

1 C. buttermilk
1 small cucumber
1 green onion
dillweed
pepper

Put all ingredients in blender, mix briefly, then chill well. This is the equivalent of 1 glass of milk.

DRINKS

TOMATO SMASH

8 oz. tomato juice
4 or 5 ice cubes
garlic powder
salt, pepper

dill seed, parsley
lemon slice
dehydrated onion flakes

You need a blender for this. First put dehydrated onion flakes to soak in a little water until soft. Put juice, ice cubes, and as much or as little herbs as you like, into the blender. Let it puree to the consistency of a milk shake. Pour into a glass and add the lemon slice.

To make it thicker, boil juice to half its volume, cool, and then prepare smash.

For an unusual dinner appetizer, dissolve a beef or chicken bouillon cube into thickened tomato juice and let cool. Then blend with ice and herbs, garnish with lemon slice and serve in a cup or bowl with a spoon. Your guests will think it's unusual and delicious! This recipe equals 8 oz. tomato juice.

RUM RUNNER

1/4 C. lime juice
3 dashes bitters
Sweetener to equal 1/4 C. sugar

2 C. crushed ice
1/2 t. rum extract

Put all ingredients into blender. Blend at high speed for 10 to 15 seconds. Serve in cocktail glass. For an unusual touch, serve in a cup with a cinnamon stirrer. UNLIMITED!

SLIM & TRIM MALTED

1 C. skim milk
2/3 t. powdered coffee

sweetener to taste
3 ice cubes

Place ingredients in blender for 30 seconds or until foamy. Also try using fresh or frozen fruit instead of coffee.

PINEAPPLE FIZZ

1 C. buttermilk
1/2 C. crushed pineapple, juice pack

1/2 t. vanilla
2 T. liquid sweetener
Dash of salt

Combine all ingredients and freeze in ice cube tray. When ready to serve, place 3 or 4 cubes in a tall glass and fill with our gingerale, red pop, or club soda. Entire recipe equals one fruit and your milk for the day. Once they're frozen you may put them in a plastic bag for ready use. A cool way to drink your milk!

fruit and your milk for the day. Once they're frozen you may put them in a plastic bag for ready use. A cool way to drink your milk!

MOCHA ICE

1 C. strong coffee (chilled)
4 oz. club soda
1 C. skim milk

Drop of maple flavoring
1/2 C. cracked ice

Combine all ingredients in blender and whip together for a long tall cooler. Equals 1 glass milk.

BIG ORANGE

1/2 C. orange juice
1/2 C. club soda or carbonated water
2 t. lemon juice

1/2 C. cracked ice
1 drop almond extract
(optional)
sweetener if desired

Combine first three ingredients and pour over ice in a tall glass. Equals 1 fruit.

GREENLAND COOLER
(see Lime Sherbet under Desserts)

Cut frozen lime sherbet into 16 chunks. Put 2 chunks in a tall glass and add 8 oz. club soda or one of our sugar-free pops. Four chunks equal 1 C. milk. Sherbet chunks may be put through blender before adding liquid.

PUNCH FOR THE BUNCH

1½ C. diced rhubarb
Sweetener to equal 1/2 C. sugar
1½ C. water

1/2 C. pineapple juice
16 oz. Our Red Punch Pop

Combine rhubarb, and water and cook until tender. Puree in blender, cool, add sweetener and other ingredients and pour over ice. Entire recipe equals 1 serving of fruit. Double this recipe for ½ gallon of punch that goes from the patio to the wedding punch bowl. Make plenty-they'll all be back for seconds! Add red food coloring if desired. Entire recipe equals 1 fruit.

KRAUT TAIL

1 C. tomato juice
1/2 C. sauerkraut with juice
1 t. dry minced onion

1 T. parsley flakes
1 C. cracked ice

Combine all ingredients and liquefy in blender. Add a
little zip with 1/4 t. dill weed on 1/4 t. basil. Like
it sweet? Add a dash of sweetener!

RASPBERRY SHRUB

1/2 C. berries (your choice)   Dash of salt
sweetener to taste   1 C. cold milk
1 T. lemon juice

Blend together 30 seconds. Equals 1 fruit and 1 milk.

MINT TULEP

1/2 C. lemon juice   1 T. dehydrated mint leaves
Sweetener to equal 1/2 C. sugar   6 C. Our gingerale
1/2 C. water

Combine water and mint leaves and simmer together for five
minutes. Add other ingredients and serve over ice.

MULLED APRÉS SKI DRINK

2 C. Our gingerale   3 whole cloves
1/8 t. nutmeg   ½ stick cinnamon

Combine and heat to boiling point. Cover and let stand
15 minutes. Reheat and pour into 2 mugs. A taste treat
even if you don't ski!

VIENNA WOODS COFFEE

7 T. instant coffee   7 C. boiling water
1 T. whole cloves   Sweetener as desired
2 1/2 stick cinnamon

Place instant coffee in a saucepan. Add cloves and
cinnamon, and pour boiling water over all. Cover and
bring to a boil. Remove from heat and let steep for
5-8 minutes. Strain into preheated coffee server and add
sweetener if desired. Serve hot with a dollop of Fluff
and a sprinkling of cinnamon.

GRAPEVINE FOR A SWINGING CROWD

1 package grape flavored un-   Sweetener to equal 1 C.
  sweetened drink mix   sugar
1 package raspberry flavored   8 C. water
  unsweetened drink mix   1 C. orange juice, un-
1 C. unsweetened crushed   sweetened
  pineapple

Combine all ingredients and serve in tall glasses over ice.
Entire recipe equals 4 fruit servings. Makes 2 1/2 quarts.

SPECIAL TEA OF THE HOUSE

2-1/2 C. boiling water
2 T. tea or 4 large tea bags
1/4 t. allspice

1/4 t. cinnamon
1/4 t. nutmeg
sweetener to equal 1 C.
 sugar

Pour boiling water over tea and spices. Cover; steep 5
minutes. Strain add sugar substitute. Good hot or cold.

CREAM SODA

1 bottle club soda
1/2 t. vanilla extract

1/2 t. liquid sweetener,
 or to taste

Mix together gently and serve on the rocks.

RED POP

1 bottle club soda
1/2 t. liquid sweetener,
 or to taste

1/2 t. cherry flavored
 unsweetened drink powder

Mix gently and serve over ice. Be creative! Try rum,
maple or any fruit flavor for a tangy pick me up!

LEMONADE

2 T. reconstituted lemon juice
1 C. water

sweetener to equal 2 T.
 sugar

Mix together and add ice cubes.

LIMEADE

4 T. reconstituted lime juice
1 C. water

sweetener to equal 2 T.
 sugar

Mix together and add ice cubes. Try club soda in place of
water with this recipe and treat your tastebuds!

CRYSTAL CLEAR TEA

2 quart pitcher of water   8 tea bags

Dangle the tea bags in the pitcher of water in the refrigerator over night. In the morning you've got tea that
never gets cloudy.

SUNSHINE TEA

2 quart pitcher of water   8 tea bags

Dangle the tea bags in the pitcher of water and set out doors. It only takes a couple of hours in the summer time to produce a full-bodied tea. You may increase the recipe to accommodate your largest kettle if you've a crowd coming!

GRASSHOPPER

1 C. crushed ice
1/3 C. dry milk powder
1/3 C. water

3 drops green food coloring
1/8 t. peppermint flavoring

Combine all ingredients in blender until thick. Eat with a spoon or drink with a straw. Boy, is this good! Try freezing this for a great dessert. Entire recipe equals one serving of milk.

CITRUS SPARKLER

2 oranges, peeled, seeded, and quartered
1/2 lemon, peeled, seeded, and quartered
2 limes, peeled, seeded, and quartered
1 C. unsweetened pineapple, chunks or crushed
1 C. water

Combine in blender and process until all are liquefied and smooth. Pour 4 ounces into a tall glass, add ice cubes and fill with carbonated water, or club soda, stir gently and enjoy. Entire recipe equals four fruit servings. You may wish to add sweetener. This can be your answer to holiday cocktails with dinners!

PINEAPPLE MILKSHAPE

1/3 C. dry powdered milk   three ice cubes
6 ounces water   Sweetener to taste
12-14 chunks of unsweetened pineapple in its own juice

Blend until foamy. This equals 1 milk and 1 fruit for the day. If you can wait long enough, put the entire mixture in your freezer tray and freeze. Just before serving break into chunks and put through blender again and serve in parfait glasses.

OUR RED PUNCH POP

2 C. club soda
2-4 packets sweetener

1 t. punch flavor dry
  drink mix, unsweetened

Dissolve drink powder in a little hot water. Add sweetener,
then club soda. Serve over ice.

PEACH DESSERT IN A HURRY

1 peach, diced
2 T. club soda

1/3 C. evaporated skimmed
  milk

Combine all ingredients in a blender and run at medium
speed until mixture is well blended. Drink chilled or
eat with a spoon if it is semi-frozen. Recipe equals
1 fruit and 2/3 C. milk.

PINK LADY

2 C. crushed ice
1 t. pink lemonade drink mix

1/2 t. brandy extract
Sweetener to equal 1/4
  C. sugar

Put all ingredients into blender. Blend at high speed for
10 to 15 seconds. Serve as you would any cocktail. Not
only is this tasty but also solves your cocktail problem.

CRANBERRY PUNCH

3 C. cranberry juice
1 package strawberry flavored
 dry drink mix, unsweetened
Sweetener to equal 1 C. sugar

1 quart ice or water or
  combination thereof
2 C. our red pop or
  gingerale

To make cranberry juice: simmer together 2 C. cranberries,
3 C. water for about 15 minutes. Strain, add sweetener to
equal ½ C. sugar. To complete the punch, add the ice or
water, rest of sweetener if desired, and chill well. Just
before serving add the red pop or gingerale. Entire recipe
equals 4 fruit servings, and makes about 9 cups of punch.
This is not only sparkling and delicious but also solves the
problem of your cocktails at parties.

OUR GINGERALE

½ t. ginger
3 packets sweetener

2 C. club soda

Dissolve ginger in a little hot water. Add sweetener, club
soda, pour over ice. Has a bite to it!

DRESSINGS & SPREADS

DIJON GARLIC SAUCE

3 T. prepared Dijon (hot) mustard
1 C . skim milk
1 whole garlic clove, peeled
1-1/2 T. lemon juice

2 beef bouillon cubes
Salt, pepper to taste
Dash of thyme

Pre-soak 2 bouillon cubes in 2 tablespoons boiling water
until soft. Heat mustard over a very low flame in a
heavy skillet and stir in the skim milk. Add whole garlic,
lemon, beef bouillon, salt, pepper, and thyme. Simmer
about 10 minutes. Do not boil. Remove garlic before
serving. Very good over broccoli or asparagus.

This is wonderful with any meat or fish dish. For variety
try finely diced pimiento or several dill seeds in the
sauce.

Entire quantity of sauce equals 1 cup of milk. Remember
to deduct ingredients from your daily milk allowance.

BLACKBERRY JELLY

2 C. blackberries
1/2 C. water
1 envelope unflavored gelatin

1/4 C. water
Sweetener to equal 1/3
 C. sugar
Ice

Simmer blackberries and water together until the berries
are soft, about 15 minutes. Strain out the seeds by
draining the berry juice through a wire strainer and
mashing the berries against the strainer with the back
of a spoon. Return to the pan. Add gelatin which has
been softened on 1/4 cup of water and stir over low heat
to dissolve gelatin. Add sweetener and pour into a pint
jar or 2-cup measure and add ice cubes to fill the measure.
Pour into 4 custard cups. This recipe equals FOUR fruits.
Try a spoonful on your breakfast toast!

ZIPPY ZERO

3 C. tomato juice
3/4 C. cider vinegar
1 T. horseradish
1 T. onion flakes
1 T. red or green pepper flakes
1 T. parsley flakes
Dash of sweetener
1 clove garlic

May add as desired:
Cloves
Allspice
Dry mustard
Garlic powder
Bay leaf
Hot pepper sauce
Oregano
Worcestershire sauce

Mix desired ingredients together in a quart jar. Store in refrigerator and use on salads, in cooking, etc. Aging seems to improve the flavor and thicken it, so if you make two quarts at a time, one will have the opportunity to age. Also, this will use one large (46 oz.) can of tomato juice.

DRESSING VINAIGRETTE

4 oz. vinegar
2 oz. water

1 oz. soy sauce

Put into jar with lid. Add garlic powder, oregano, pepper, bay leaf, and sweetener as desired. Shake well, let chill. Wonderful on tossed salad!

SLIM & TRIM MAYONNAISE

1-1/2 t. lemon juice
1-1/2 t. sweetener
1 T. yellow salad mustard
2 t. horseradish
1 t. Worcestershire
1 t. soy sauce

1 T. dehydrated onion
   flakes
1 T. parsley flakes
1/2 t. celery seed
1/4 t. onion juice
   (optional)
1 C. buttermilk

Put all ingredients in a small bowl. Stir well, then start adding the buttermilk slowly. This keeps well in the refrigerator, and the entire recipe equals 1 cup of milk.

Other interesting additions might be: dillweed, garlic salt, onion salt, and celery salt. If you prefer, you may use garlic powder and onion powder.

"REALLY" ROQUEFORT DRESSING

1 C. buttermilk
1 t. dry mustard
1 t. salt

1 T. dry onion flakes
1 T. celery seed

Gradually add buttermilk to the dry ingredients. The older and thicker the buttermilk, the better the dressing! The first day this is sensational roquefort. The second day it's an even better celery cream dressing. The entire recipe equals one cup of milk.

NIPPY NERO DRESSING

1 package unflavored gelatin
1/2 C. cold water
Sweetener to equal 1/4 C. sugar
1 T. dry mustard

1 T. salt
1/4 t. paprika
1/2 C. vinegar

Soften gelatin in cold water. Mix together all the remaining ingredients with the exception of the vinegar. Add to the first mixture with 1 and 1/3 cup boiling water in the top of a double boiler. Cook until gelatin is dissolved. Stir in vinegar. Beat well. Store in refrigerator. This sets up firm, so when you wish to serve, remove from refrigerator half an hour before serving time. This is absolutely marvelous on fruit or green salad.

CAPE COD DRESSING

1/2 C. tomato juice (1 C. cooked down to 1/2 C.)
1 t. horseradish
1 t. lemon juice

1/2 t. Worcestershire sauce
Dash of Tabasco sauce
Pinch of red, hot pepper

Combine and let stand for flavor mix. Serve hot over baked fish. Add artificial sweetener to taste to make a delicious cold shrimp cocktail sauce.

KETCHIP

3-1/2 C. tomato juice
1-1/2 C. vinegar
2" stick cinnamon
1 t. peppercorns
1 t. whole cloves
1 t. allspice berries
1 t. celery seed

1 T. salt
2 t. paprika
1/4 t. cayenne pepper
2 envelopes unflavored gelatin
1/2 C. cold water
Sweetener to equal 3/4 C. sugar

Put spices in a square of cloth and tie it up, or use a metal container for loose tea to hold the spices. Simmer together for half an hour, to extract the spice flavors with the vinegar, 1 C. of the tomato juice. Soften gelatin on cold water and add to the above hot mix. Stir until dissolved and add the sweetener and the remaining 2-1/2 C. of cold tomato juice. Remove the spice container. Store in refrigerator. Makes about 1 quart of thick, cold ketchip. Use anytime you want ketchip taste!

A FASTER KETCHIP

INSTEAD OF:
2" stick cinnamon
1 t. peppercorns
1 t. whole cloves
1 t. allspice berries

USE:
1/4 t. ground cinnamon
1/4 t. black pepper
1/4 t. ground cloves
1/4 t. ground allspice

Mix all spices including substitutions with vinegar and 1 cup of the tomato juice. Bring to a boil. Add softened gelatin and sweetener and stir to dissolve. Pour in the

other 2-1/2 C. of tomato juice. Chill in refrigerator. The
color of this ketchip will be a bit darker from the ground
spices and the taste a little bitier, and because it isn't
boiled any length of time, you'll have about 1/2 cup more
in volume. Tastes like catsup, won't keep you overweight,
and for a salad in a hurry, moisten chilled French-style
green beans with a dab of this.

LOMAIZE

2 t. onion salt
2 t. dry mustard
Sweetener to equal 1/4 C. sugar
1/4 t. black pepper
3/4 C. cider vinegar
1 envelope unflavored gelatin

3/4 C. cold water
1 C. skim milk
1 T. onion flakes
2 drops yellow food
  coloring

Mix first five ingredients together and bring to a boil.
Add the gelatin which has been softened on cold water, and
stir well to dissolve. Add the onion flakes and skim milk
and desired amount of food coloring. Let set in refrigerator, and when thick, beat well in blender and then store
in refrigerator. 2 T. equals 1 T. skim milk, so deduct
from your daily milk allowance. LoMaize makes it so easy
to have tuna salad, chicken salad, etc.

MINOR THOUSAND ISLAND DRESSING

1 t. onion salt
1 t. dry mustard
1 t. paprika
1 t. celery seed
3/4 C. tomato juice
1/4 C. vinegar
1 envelope unflavored gelatin
1/2 C. water

Sweetener to equal 1/4
  C. sugar
1 C. skim milk
1 dill pickle, minced
  fine
1 T. green or red pepper
  flakes
3 T. chopped pimiento
  (optional)
1 T. chives (optional)

Soften gelatin on 1/2 C. water. In saucepan, combine first
six ingredients and bring to a boil. Dissolve softened
gelatin in hot solution, and add skim milk and sweetener.
Let set until firm. Whip in blender and fold in minced
pickle and pepper flakes softened on 1 T. water. Add pimiento and chives if desired. 2 tablespoons equals 1 tablespoon skim milk to be deducted from daily allowance. This
is a great dressing for head lettuce salad at lunch or
dinner!

CARROT SPREAD

1 lb. carrots, cut up
2 T. dry green bell pepper
2 T. water

2 green onions, tops and all
1/2 C. LoMaize, room temperature
2 T. salad mustard

Soften pepper in water and combine with carrots, onions, Lo-
Maize and salad mustard in blender. Chop until all are
blended together, stopping the motor to push it into the
center as necessary. This spread will keep a week or more
in the refrigerator, and makes the prettiest stuffed celery
imaginable. Use it for dip for cauliflowerettes, radishes,
pepper strips, etc.

HORSERADISH SAUCE

1/2 C. LoMaize
1 dill pickle, diced

1 T. horseradish
1 T. Dijon mustard

Combine all ingredients in a serving bowl. A wonderful
sauce for fish as well as beef.

TARTAR SAUCE

1/2 C. LoMaize
2 T. dry parsley flakes
1 dill pickle, minced

1-1/2 T. lemon juice
1 T. dry onion flakes

Beat together and chill. Any leftover may be stored in
the refrigerator, and beaten again before serving time.
Tastes better than the fattening kind, because you have
peace of mind and no guilty feeling with this kind!

DRESSING FOR A FRUIT SALAD

1/2 t. unflavored gelatin
2 T. cold water
2/3 C. hot water
2 T. vinegar
1/2 t. prepared mustard (salad
   mustard)

1/2 t. celery seed
1/2 t. salt
1/4 t. ginger
Sweetener to equal 1 T.
   sugar

Soften gelatin on cold water, dissolve in hot water. Add
remaining ingredients, mix well and refrigerate. Remove
from refrigerator half an hour before serving time and beat.

SEASONED SALT

5 T. iodized salt
1/2 t. dried thyme leaves
1/2 t. marjoram
1/2 t. garlic salt
2-1/2 t. paprika
1/2 t. curry powder

1 t. dry mustard
1/2 t. onion powder
1/8 t. dill seed
1/2 t. celery seed
1/2 t. oregano
2 T. parsley flakes

Put all ingredients into blender and process until blended.
This keeps forever, and sprinkled on chicken the last 15
minutes of baking, makes the best "fried" chicken ever
tasted.

MARINADE FOR CHICKEN OR FISH

1/4 C. white vinegar
2 T. lemon juice
1 T. dry onion flakes

1 T. horseradish
2 t. powdered ginger

Combine and simmer for 2 minutes. Spread on chicken and
let set at room temperature for 1/2 hour before broiling.
It's yummy!

MINT SAUCE

1/2 C. white vinegar
Sweetener to equal 1/4 C. sugar

2 T. dry mint flakes

Heat together, let stand one hour and strain before using
as a sauce for lamb. Leftover lamb heated up in this
tastes great, too.

RUSSIAN DRESSING

Mix equal parts Ketchip and LoMaize!

GREEN GODDESS DRESSING

1/2 C. LoMaize
1 clove garlic
6 green onions with tops

1 T. lemon juice
1 T. tarragon vinegar
2 T. chopped chives

Beat together in blender, store in refrigerator. Great on
salads!

CHICKEN BAR-B-Q SAUCE

1 medium onion, chopped
1 C. Zippy Zero
1/4 t. ground cloves
1/4 t. cinnamon
1/4 t. ground allspice

1/2 T. dry mustard
1/4 t. garlic powder
1/4 t. hot crushed peppers
Sweetener as desired

Simmer together until thickened. Use hot on chicken on the broiler or on the grill, adding during the last 15-20 minutes of cooking. Really scrumptious!

CUCUMBER DRESSING FOR COLD FISH

1 medium cucumber	1/4 t. dillweed
1 T. lemon juice	1/4 C. LoMaize
1 t. salt	

Chop first four ingredients together in blender until the cucumber is finely grated. Stir in LoMaize. If the cucumber hasn't been waxed, don't peel it! The green taste is good. This recipe will make 1-1/2 C. of sauce, more or less, depending on the size of the cucumber!

TOMATO-MUSHROOM SAUCE

4 oz. Zippy Zero	2 fresh green onions,
1 can mushrooms, drained	chopped

Simmer ingredients together for about 5 minutes. Serve over pancakes or use to baste fish or chicken or steak. You'll find many uses for this combo.

APPLE BUTTER

2 apples (about 1/2 lb.)	1/4 t. cloves
1 C. water	1/4 t. nutmeg or allspice
1 T. lemon juice	Sweetener to equal 1/4 C.
1/2 t. cinnamon	sugar

Wash, quarter, and core apples. Slice thin, or dice and put in a saucepan with water and seasonings. Simmer slowly, or until they're well cooked. Put through a food mill or blender, return to heat and add sugar substitute. This recipe equals two fruit servings.

BARBEQUE SAUCE

8 oz. tomato juice	Pinch of parsley, pepper
1/2 C. minced onion	Dash of bitters
1 bay leaf	1/2 C. soy sauce
1 T. lemon juice	Sweetener to taste
Garlic salt, powder, or juice	Chili powder if you like
to taste	it hot!

To make a very thick sauce, put 1 package of cooked French-style green beans through blender until smooth. Add to sauce until of desired consistency.

ANOTHER GODDESS DRESSING

1 medium eggplant
1 C. boiling water
1 T. onion flakes
1 package unflavored gelatin
1/4 C. dill pickle juice or
    vinegar
Sweetener to equal 1/4 C. sugar

2 t. salt
1 T. dry mustard
1/4 t. paprika, pepper
1/2 C. dill pickle juice
2 or 3 drops green food
    coloring

Pare the eggplant and cut into 1/2" cubes. Add water and
onion flakes and cook until soft, about 15 minutes. Add
gelatin softened in juice and stir thoroughly to dissolve.
Add sweetener and puree in blender. Combine salt, mustard,
paprika, pepper and juice. Blend well. Tint to desired
shade of green. Very good on lettuce, tossed salad, etc.,
and is unlimited.

SPICY FRENCH DRESSING

1 C. our Ketchip
1/2 C. lemon juice

1 chicken bouillon cube
1/2 C. boiling water

Dissolve bouillon cube in boiling water. Add remaining ingredients, chill. Some of our all-time losers think this
is reason enough to make Ketchip!

SPIRITED "76" DRESSING

7 oz. (total) sauerkraut and juice
6 oz. tomato juice
2 teaspoons horseradish

Put in blender and mix until it is the consistency you like.
Really perks up that tossed salad. Store in jar in refrigerator.

Dairy Queen - 1 Serving
1/2 C cold water. - 1 envelope of Knox Gelatine (Softened
cold water. Note: Pour cold water in blender, add
gelatine. Add 1/4 C boiling water to blender, add Sweet-
ner, 1/4 t. Vanilla - 2/3 C dry milk. Add fruit (2
slices of pineapple (yellow Label) packed in its own
juice or any frozen fruit allotment to add to
1 fruit, peach 2 halves or 1 C frozen or fresh Strawbe-
Blend and add 2 ice cubes and blend until thick.
very good. This is your milk allotment for the
day, use Sweet & Low very little. Its filling and a
treat.

WEEKLY PROGRESS CHART

Date	Weight	Loss	Date	Weight	Loss